HUMAN LINKS
TO COASTAL DISASTERS

D0955120

THE
HEINZ
CENTER

**THE H. JOHN HEINZ III CENTER FOR
SCIENCE, ECONOMICS AND THE ENVIRONMENT**

The H. John Heinz III Center for Science, Economics and the Environment

Established in December 1995 in honor of Senator John Heinz, The Heinz Center is a nonprofit institution dedicated to improving the scientific and economic foundation for environmental policy through multisectoral collaboration. Focusing on issues that are likely to confront policymakers within two to five years, the Center creates and fosters collaboration among industry, environmental organizations, academia, and government in each of its program areas and projects. The membership of the Center's Board of Trustees, its steering committees, and all its committees and working groups reflects its guiding philosophy: that all relevant parties must be involved if the complex issues surrounding environmental policymaking are to be resolved. The Center's mission is to identify emerging environmental issues, conduct related scientific research and economic analyses, and create and disseminate nonpartisan policy options for solving environmental problems.

About the Social Consequences of Coastal Hazards Study

The Heinz Center's Social Consequences of Coastal Hazards study was conducted under the terms of a joint project agreement between The Heinz Center and the National Oceanic and Atmospheric Administration's Coastal Services Center. This report does not necessarily reflect the policies or views of the organizations or agencies that employ the panel members and study sponsors.

Library of Congress Control Number: 2002111207

International Standard Book Number: 0-9717592-2-7

06 05 04 03 02   5 4 3 2 1

Printed in the United States of America

Additional copies of this report may be obtained free of charge from

The Heinz Center
1001 Pennsylvania Avenue, N.W., Suite 735 South, Washington, D.C. 20004
Telephone (202) 737-6307   Fax (202) 737-6410   e-mail info@heinzctr.org

This report is also available in full at www.heinzctr.org

Cover Illustration: "Expecting Thunder." Monotype copyright © 1994 by Mary Edna Fraser.

Human Links
to Coastal Disasters

Heinz Center Staff

Thomas E. Lovejoy, President
Jeannette Aspden, Corporate Secretary
Sarah Baish, Research Associate (through 1/15/02)
Melissa Brown, Staff Assistant
Kent Cavender-Bares, Fellow and Research Associate
Pierre-Marc Daggett, Research Associate and Travel Coordinator
Sheila David, Senior Fellow and Project Manager
Mary C. Eng, Treasurer
Robert Friedman, Vice President for Research
Judy Goss, Research Assistant
Cheryl A. Graham, Senior Fellow and Project Manager
Anthony Janetos, Senior Fellow
Robin O'Malley, Senior Fellow and Project Manager
Elissette Rivera, Research Assistant
P. J. Simmons, Fellow

CONTENTS

PREFACE

MOST DISASTER LOSSES do not stem from unexpected events. Rather, they are the predictable results of interactions among the physical environment, the social and demographic characteristics of the communities experiencing them, and the built environment. It has become increasingly clear that problems associated with natural hazards cannot be solved in isolation—they are symptoms of broader, more basic social and political issues. Vulnerability analysis has shifted from an emphasis on nature as the cause of disasters toward more contextual approaches to understanding the role that humans play in creating vulnerability (Anderson 2000). As documented in a recent national assessment, *Disasters by Design*, short-sighted and narrow conceptions of the human relationship to the natural environment account for the nation's failure to reduce the extent to which natural hazards result in disasters (Mileti 1999).

Human vulnerability, or those circumstances that place people at risk while reducing their means of response, and its links to the physical and natural environment are integral concerns in the development of disaster policies. To be effective, mitigation must address the social and economic factors at the heart of risk and vulnerability. Communities, households, and individuals need to know the range of alternatives available to them and understand fully the implications of their decisions. Further, there must be a collective will to seek more sustainable ways of development and resource utilization.

In 1999, another Heinz Center panel completed an analysis of methods for understanding and accounting for the true costs of weather-related coastal hazards (Heinz Center 2000b). The panel developed a framework for community-level risk and vulnerability assessment that factors in relevant but rarely considered economic, social, environmental, and regulatory issues. Particular attention was given to developing an understanding of the full range of unreported or hidden economic costs of coastal hazards.

Cost assessments are an important component of decisions made to reduce societal and environmental exposure to coastal hazard impacts, but traditional assessment methods generally have not incorporated many of the social, economic, and environmental costs, nor have evaluations of potential measures for mitigating future losses considered these impacts. Conventional risk assessment has tended to emphasize what has been (or can be) measured quantitatively. Most of the social costs associated with coastal hazards, for example, go unrecognized in official assessments, in part because they are difficult to define and count. To estimate the social costs of any major disaster event, it is necessary to examine the effects on social institutions, such as a community's families, schools, and places of worship, as well as the social networks connecting groups and people— not a simple task.

Following the publication of *The Hidden Costs of Coastal Hazards* and discussions of the study's findings at various conferences and meetings, The Heinz Center developed a proposal for a follow-on study focusing on the human links to coastal disasters. While most coastal hazards are wind- and water-related, the panel also chose to briefly discuss earthquakes since they pose an additional risk to many coastal areas. Even though most of the examples throughout the report have to do with hurricanes and flooding, the panel used examples from the Loma Prieta and Northridge earthquakes when they were good illustrations of the topics under discussion. The National Oceanic and Atmospheric Administration's Coastal Services Center assisted in refining the scope of work and is the sponsor of this study. The members of the panel served on a volunteer basis to work on this project over an 18-month period and met three times. A fourth meeting was held with chapter leaders in Washington, D.C., to finalize the report.

We would like to take this opportunity to express our gratitude to Sheila David, our project manager and an early advocate of the study, without whose outstanding leadership and persistent prodding the work never would have been completed. We also owe a debt to Sarah Baish (former research associate) and Judy Goss (current research assistant) at The Heinz Center for their work on behalf of this project. We are grateful to the Coastal Services Center for its support, and to Paul Scholz, in

particular, for his belief in the importance of the project and his willing-
ness to serve on the panel. A special thanks to those who accepted major
writing assignments, including Susan Cutter, Dennis Smith, Josephine
Malilay, Marilyn Self, and Howard Kunreuther. Other panel members
contributing to this project include Timothy Beatley, Lloyd Cluff, Robert
Collins, Laurie Johnson, Robert G. Lee, Donna Moffitt, Michael K.
Orbach, Douglas Rader, and Jackie Savitz. Working with outstanding
scholars from a variety of fields who were open to new ways of looking at
vulnerability was a rewarding and enlightening experience.

Within a broad vulnerability framework, this report examines
human factors influencing vulnerability, beginning with policies and
practices that drive coastal development. Subsequent chapters make a
unique contribution to the study of hazards and disasters by bringing
together what is known about their effects on people, from changes in the
physical well-being of individuals to impacts on the social institutions of
communities and regions.

The report also explores how actions that typically take place following a disaster affect future risk and vulnerability. The dominant theme
throughout is the need to build disaster resiliency through increased
awareness and promotion of the social factors that are the essence of
human communities. In the final analysis, disaster-resilient communities
are sustainable communities—and good places to live.

BETTY HEARN MORROW
Chair

ACKNOWLEDGMENTS

MANY INDIVIDUALS assisted the panel in its task by participating in panel meetings, providing data and background information, reviewing and editing drafts, and recommending individuals to be interviewed. We express our appreciation to the following people for their invaluable contributions to this project:

Jeannette Aspden, The Heinz Center
Jerad Bales, U.S. Geological Survey
Brenda L. Bruun, Center for Mental Health Service
Larry Crowder, Duke University
Robert Friedman, The Heinz Center
Billy Ray Hall, North Carolina Rural Economic Development Center
Cynthia Hughes, Touchstone Counseling Services
Lynn Muchmore, North Carolina General Assembly
Laura Ost, consulting editor, Arlington, VA
Brenda Phillips, Jacksonville State University
Stan Riggs, East Carolina University
Gavin Smith, North Carolina Division of Emergency Management
Patricia Stukes, Jacksonville State University
Mark Taylor, State Farm Insurance Companies
Jerry Walters, Town of Oak Island, NC
John Whitehead, East Carolina University

The Heinz Center appreciates the thoughtful critiques provided by the reviewers. The reviewers do not, however, necessarily approve, disapprove, or endorse this report. The Heinz Center assumes full responsibility for the report and the accuracy of its contents and acknowledges the contributions of the following reviewers: Todd Miller, North Carolina Coastal Federation, Newport, North Carolina; Sarah Nathe, University of California, Berkeley; Brenda Phillips, Jacksonville State University, Jacksonville, Alabama; James Russell, Institute for Business Home and Safety, Tampa, Florida; and Libby Smith, North Carolina Division of Emergency Management, Raleigh.

SUMMARY

THE UNIQUE physical environment of the world's coasts, combined with the rapid rise in human habitation and structural development along the coastlines, create a complex set of circumstances that place individuals and communities at risk. To date, most efforts to reduce coastal vulnerability have focused on the hazards, the built environment, or the biophysical environment. Human vulnerability—the result of circumstances that place people at risk, reduce their means of response, or deny them protection—is an integral concern in the development and evaluation of disaster policies. This study is directed toward the goal of more disaster-resistant coastal communities, beginning at the level of individual households and neighborhoods. Building upon the Framework for Community Planning developed in an earlier Heinz Center report, *Hidden Costs of Coastal Hazards* (Heinz Center 2000b), this investigation covers new ground by focusing on the social construct of vulnerability. Areas of concern in this study are the human vulnerability of coastal communities, with emphasis on identification of high-risk populations; human impacts of disasters, including the mental and physical health effects on individuals; and the impacts of natural disasters on the social institutions that make up our coastal communities.

UNDERSTANDING HUMAN LINKS TO COASTAL DISASTERS

The significance of the focus on human links to coastal disasters is two-fold. First, improved understanding of human factors is an important step

1

toward designing and implementing effective mitigation initiatives, but this tends to be overlooked in a rush to seek more obvious answers that do not address the root causes of coastal vulnerability. Second, knowledge about human and social impacts of past disasters on specific populations and communities can inform disaster response at all stages, including long-term recovery and mitigation efforts.

Three types of vulnerabilities—biophysical, built, and human—increase the risk of coastal hazards at any given place. To understand the impact of coastal hazards on people and the places where they live, one first needs to be aware of the driving forces that reduce or exacerbate each type of vulnerability. The vulnerability framework, adapted by the panel from the work of Susan Cutter (1996) in Chapter 2, provides an overview of factors influencing the three types of vulnerability and how they interact to determine the overall vulnerability of a place to a coastal disaster.

Human vulnerability stems from the individual characteristics of people that make them more susceptible to harm from environmental threats (age, gender, race, health, and personal habits). There is increasing recognition that certain social and economic characteristics influence human vulnerability at both individual and community levels. Lack of economic or human resources can limit the ability of some groups, such as woman-headed households, the elderly, the unemployed, the illiterate or uneducated, the ill or handicapped, to respond adequately to a coastal hazard. Minorities and other marginalized groups may be excluded from lines of communication and action. Housing status, such as being a renter, can also limit an individual's ability to respond. Community-level factors, such as intensity and type of residential, commercial, or industry development, infrastructure and lifelines, and population growth, also affect hazard vulnerability. Table S.1 summarizes what is known about social and economic characteristics that influence human vulnerability at both individual and community levels.

CONCLUSIONS AND RECOMMENDATIONS

The unique contribution of this report is that it focuses on how human actions and decisions related to coastal settlement in areas prone to natural disasters have placed increasing populations at risk. After identifying factors influencing coastal development and population vulnerability, it brings together findings on the impacts on individuals and communities.

Recommendations for specific policy or program enhancements are then provided in support of each finding. These conclusions and recommendations, summarized below, offer the academic community, public policy makers, and emergency managers opportunities to better understand and assess variations in vulnerability among individuals and communities and to develop policies and programs that promise lasting reduction of human vulnerability to coastal hazards.

HUMAN VULNERABILITY

Conceptually we know many of the social and economic characteristics that influence human vulnerability at the individual and community level. The systematic assessment of these characteristics in any given coastal location will help communities better identify and address human vulnerability to coastal disasters. Tools such as the framework for assessing vulnerability (Figure 2.1, p. 30) and the population characteristics influencing social vulnerability (Table S.1) will help identify vulnerable populations, but additional research is needed to better understand and define the most vulnerable individuals and populations.

■ **Public and private support should promote research to better understand how individual factors known to influence human vulnerability work, and the findings used by emergency managers and disaster responders to address the needs of specific groups and places.**

Many of the forces driving coastal development, which increase the vulnerability of the human, built, and biophysical environments, are encouraged by federal, state, and local governmental policies and practices and by fractured jurisdictions in coastal environments.

■ **Federal initiatives such as the Robert T. Stafford Disaster Relief and Emergency Assistance Act, National Flood Insurance Program, beach nourishment programs, tax incentives for second homes, and infrastructure projects, as well as relevant state and local policies and practices, should be reexamined by legislative and executive bodies at all levels to reduce their role as possible stimulators of coastal growth and enhancers of vulnerability in known hazardous areas. Human and social costs should be part of the benefit–cost analysis used to determine any project's viability. Similarly, vulnerability**

TABLE S.1 Population Characteristics Influencing Social Vulnerability

Population Characteristic	Description	Increases (+) or Decreases (−) Social Vulnerability
Socioeconomic status (income, political power, prestige)	Status affects the ability to absorb losses and enhance resilience to hazard impacts. Wealth enables communities to absorb and recover from losses more quickly using insurance, social safety nets, and entitlement programs.	High status (+/−) Low income or status (+) (*Sources*: Cutter et al. 2000, Peacock et al. 2000, Puente 1999, Bolin and Stanford 1998, Blaikie et al. 1994, Burton et al. 1993)
Gender	Women often have a more difficult time during recovery than men because of sector-specific employment (e.g., personal services), lower wages, and family care responsibilities.	Gender (+) (*Sources*: Peacock et al. 2000, Enarson and Scanlon 1999, Morrow and Phillips 1999, Enarson and Morrow 1998, Hewitt 1997, Fothergill 1996, Morrow and Enarson 1996)
Race and ethnicity	These factors impose language and cultural barriers and affect access to post-disaster funding and occupation of high-hazard areas.	Non-white (+) Non-Anglo (+) (*Sources*: Pulido 2000, Peacock et al. 2000, Morrow and Phillips 1999, Bolin and Stanford 1998, Bolin 1993)
Age	Extremes of age affect the movement out of harm's way. Parents lose time and money caring for children when day care facilities are affected; the elderly may have mobility constraints or concerns that increase the burden of care and lack of resilience.	Elderly (+) Children (+) (*Sources*: Ngo 2001, Cutter et al. 2000, Hewitt 1997, O'Brien and Mileti 1992)
Commercial and industrial development	The value, quality, and density of commercial and industrial buildings provide indicators of the state of economic health of a community, potential losses in the business community, and longer-term issues with recovery after an event.	High density (+) High value (+/−) (*Sources*: Heinz Center 2000b, Webb et al. 2000)

Employment loss	The potential loss of additional employment following a disaster increases the possible number of unemployed workers in a community. Such losses contribute to a slower recovery from the disaster.	Employment loss (+) (*Source*: Mileti 1999)
Rural/urban	Rural residents may be more vulnerable because of lower incomes and more dependence on a locally based resource economy (e.g., farming or fishing). High-density areas (urban) complicate evacuation out of harm's way.	Rural (+) Urban (+) (*Sources*: Cutter et al. 2000, Cova and Church 1997)
Residential property	The value, quality, and density of residential construction affect potential losses and recovery. Expensive homes on the coast are costly to replace; mobile homes are easily destroyed and less resilient to hazards.	Mobile homes (+) (*Sources*: Cutter et al. 2000, Heinz Center 2000b, Bolin and Stanford 1991)
Infrastructure and lifelines	The loss of sewer, bridges, water, communications, and transportation infrastructure compounds potential disaster losses. The loss of infrastructure may place an insurmountable financial burden on smaller communities that lack the financial resources to rebuild.	Extensive infrastructure (+) (*Sources*: Heinz Center 2000b, Platt 1995)
Renters	People rent because they are transients, do not have the financial resources for home ownership, or do not want the responsibility of home ownership. They often lack access to information about financial aid during recovery. In extreme cases, renters lack sufficient shelter options when lodging becomes uninhabitable or too costly to afford.	Renters (+) (*Sources*: Heinz Center 2000b, Morrow 1999)

(continued)

TABLE S.1 *Continued*

Population Characteristic	Description	Increases (+) or Decreases (−) Social Vulnerability
Occupation	Some occupations, especially those involving resource extraction, may be severely affected by a hazard event. Self-employed fishermen suffer when their means of production is lost, and they may not have the requisite capital to resume work in a timely fashion; therefore, they may seek alternative employment. Migrant workers engaged in agriculture and low-skilled service jobs (housekeeping, child care, and gardening) may suffer similarly as disposable income fades and the need for services declines. Immigration status also affects occupational recovery.	Professional or managerial (−) Clerical or laborer (+) Service sector (+) (*Sources*: Heinz Center 2000b, Puente 1999, Hewitt 1997)
Family structure	Families with large numbers of dependents and single-parent households often have limited wherewithal to outsource care for dependents and thus must juggle work responsibilities and care for family members. All these factors affect resilience to and recovery from hazards.	High birth rates (+) Large families (+) Single-parent households (+) (*Sources*: Heinz Center 2000b, Morrow 1999, Puente 1999, Morrow 1997, Blaikie et al. 1994)
Education	Education is linked to socioeconomic status in that higher educational attainment affects lifetime earnings, and limited education constrains the ability to understand warning information and access recovery information.	Little education (+) Highly educated (−) (*Source*: Heinz Center 2000b)
Population growth	Counties experiencing rapid growth lack available high-quality housing, and the social services network may not have had time to adjust to increased populations. New	Rapid growth (+) (*Sources*: Cutter et al 2000, Heinz Center 2000b, Morrow 1999, Puente 1999)

	migrants may not speak the language and may not be familiar with how to deal with bureaucracies in obtaining relief or recovery information. All these factors increase vulnerability.	
Health status	The public health literature shows that people with preexisting illnesses may be at risk for death/illness/injury in disaster settings. People with preexisting cardiovascular and respiratory conditions who are exposed to smoke and haze from forest fires may be more at risk for adverse health outcomes; they also may be vulnerable to heart attacks during seismic activity.	Major health problems (+) Minor or no health problems (−) (*Sources:* Parati et al. 2001, Brauer 1999, Brown 1999, Minami et al. 1997)
Medical services	Health care providers, including physicians, nursing homes, and hospitals, are important post-event sources of relief. The lack of proximate medical services lengthens the time needed to obtain short-term relief and achieve longer-term recovery from disasters.	Higher density of medical (−) (*Sources:* Heinz Center 2000b, Morrow 1999, Hewitt 1997)
Social dependence	People who are totally dependent on social services for survival are already economically and socially marginalized and require additional support in the post-disaster period.	High dependence (+) Low dependence (−) (*Sources:* Heinz Center 2000b, Hewitt 2000, Morrow 1999, Drabek 1996)
Special-needs populations	Special-needs populations (infirm, institutionalized, transient, homeless) are difficult to identify, let alone measure and monitor. Yet it is this segment of society that invariably is left out of recovery efforts, largely because of this invisibility in communities.	Large number of special needs (+) Small number of special needs (−) (*Sources:* Morrow 1999, Tobin and Ollenburger 1993)

Source: Cutter et al. 2001.

assessments should be undertaken by all government jurisdictions as part of regular land use planning and zoning processes.

HUMAN IMPACTS

Not enough is known about the unique mechanisms that lead to specific deaths, injuries, and illnesses associated with disasters. Current information tends to be sketchy, particularly concerning the situational details associated with disasters and information about victims. To develop effective education, mitigation, and response programs, planners need a better understanding of situations that arise during disasters and health impacts on target populations.

■ **New methodologies and research initiatives should be developed by the Centers for Disease Control and other related organizations to better quantify and describe health-related outcomes of coastal disasters, identifying populations most at risk for specific problems.**

There is a growing body of evidence that many, indeed most, of the deaths and injuries associated with coastal hazards do not occur at the time of direct impact. In most hurricanes, the greatest havoc is created, not by winds and coastal surges, but rather by inland flooding. Cleanup and reconstruction activities also can be very dangerous, as evidenced by the number of chain saw accidents, falls from roofs, and other accidents reported. Because of a general lack of systematic recording, the actual number of accidents is likely to be much higher than is suggested by the data.

■ **At all levels, from federal to local, education and outreach programs should be developed to target lesser-known dangers from cleanup and reconstruction activities. Drowning as a result of driving in hazardous areas after a storm or not using flotation devices during flood rescues and injuries from the inappropriate use of chain saws, generators, and other equipment in the aftermath of an event are some of these dangers.**

The multistate traffic gridlock that occurred when millions attempted to evacuate before Hurricane Floyd highlighted the dangers associated with mass evacuation. Ways that are more effective must be found to help people realistically assess and respond to the risks, prevent unnecessary evacuation, provide safe sanctuaries closer to home, and better manage the safe evacuation of those who should leave.

- **Evacuation issues should be part of land use decisions in coastal areas. Federal and state transportation agencies need to develop multistate evacuation policies and plans for coastal areas. More research is needed to better understand how people make evacuation decisions. Technologies, such as computer modeling and the visualization of the effects of storm surge and flooding in specific locations, can help citizens evaluate their level of risk. Extensive education programs should be implemented to assist people in coastal areas to make wiser evacuation decisions, emphasizing the hazards of unnecessary or untimely evacuation. Alternatives, such as home shuttering and safe local shelters, should be promoted through loan programs, public shelter funding, and other government incentives.**

The importance of social support systems in combating the mental health effects of disasters has been well established. People recover more quickly when they are embedded in social networks of family, friends, and neighbors.

- **Response agencies at all levels should pay special attention to promoting and protecting social networks when planning policies and community response programs. To the extent possible, family and neighborhood groups should be kept together when temporary sheltering or housing is assigned. Programs and facilities should be planned to promote formal and informal social interaction in the aftermath of a disaster.**

There is no substitute for mitigation and preparedness. Not only is the impact likely to be reduced, but the psychological consequences associated with injury and damage is also lessened. Even when a person's home is damaged in spite of mitigation actions, the emotional impact tends to be lessened because those efforts had been made. People do best when they have the knowledge, resources, and opportunities to take mitigation and response actions on their own behalf.

- **Mitigation measures need to be reexamined by taking into account a broader set of impacts, including the social costs of disasters. Those initiatives shown to be cost effective should be expanded** through educational and outreach programs, special incentives, and resources to assist high-risk populations.

COMMUNITY AND INSTITUTIONAL IMPACTS

Most governments, particularly at the local level, are not prepared to deal adequately with a coastal disaster. Even when they are prepared to handle immediate emergency needs, most have not planned for recovery. This can accentuate pain and suffering, prolong recovery, create political fallout, and result in the rebuilding of unsafe communities.

■ **Governments at all levels of jurisdiction should have all-hazard disaster plans in place, including recovery plans with mitigation measures for rebuilding safer communities. Disaster planning should be developed in partnership with all interested parties and should cut across political boundaries to serve the citizens of a region.**

After an event, economic losses to the business community can be devastating to individual enterprises, especially small local businesses, and to the economy and quality of life in the community as a whole.

■ **Public and private initiatives and programs to promote effective disaster planning in the business sector, particularly for small, local businesses, should be expanded. Business disaster plans should include initiatives to assist employees and their families in preparing and responding in a timely manner. Federal, state, and local initiatives should include public–private partnerships and use a variety of means, including insurance, building codes and regulations, loans, subsidies, and economic incentives, to improve community economic resilience to hazards.**

Public concern and funding related to the care and nurturance of children tends to be limited, a reality that becomes particularly noticeable after a major disaster, when children's needs tend to be considered low priority compared to other concerns, such as economic interests. Little is known about the long-term developmental and behavioral effects on children when a community, including its educational and cultural institutions, fails to address the needs of children and youth adequately during long disaster recovery periods.

- **Every level of jurisdiction should make the needs of children and youth a higher priority throughout all stages of disaster response.** Local plans and federal response programs should be in place to assist organizations that serve children (educational, child care, recreational, cultural, health, and social services agencies) in resuming operations quickly. Although schools may need to be used as temporary shelters, they should not be used as longer-term housing for dislocated victims. Parks and recreational programs provide children with diversions from damaged homes and stressed families, leading to safer communities. The need for additional teacher assistants, social workers, and other support services for parents and educators should be anticipated as part of community disaster planning. Child care programs, including informal services, should receive high priority in community rebuilding activities. More research is needed on the long-term effects of disasters on child development and learning.

Cultural and social institutions are the heart of a community. When they are disrupted, not only are services unavailable, but communities lose much of their identity and definition. Museums, art shows, and other cultural and social events tend to be low priorities after a disaster, yet they serve important social, psychological, and educational functions.

- **Local organizations should be encouraged to hold cultural and social events throughout recovery periods. These events facilitate social networks, provide an important respite from recovery activities, serve as venues for distributing or gathering community information, help combat depression, and serve to bind communities together.**

When disaster strikes, community religious and service organizations are apt to be crippled, losing donors and volunteers at a time when they are most needed. In the United States, nonprofit organizations are well organized to enter a community to assist with recovery needs. However, they tend to operate independently, failing to work through local groups. This can reduce the effectiveness of their services, as well as undermine local organizations.

- **Governmental and nongovernmental response groups coming into a community to assist with relief and recovery should work through local churches, organizations, and agencies, building their**

capacity rather than supplanting it. Actively working with community-based organizations can reveal hidden vulnerability.

The responsibility for caring for dependent members of society, especially children and the elderly, rests almost entirely upon families—and within families, most often upon women. It is within these same family units that most disaster-related decisions and actions occur. Although women provide the bulk of caregiving, for cultural and historical reasons they often lack the economic resources and personal autonomy needed for family preparation and recovery. Households headed by women are among the poorest and most marginalized, and these high-risk households are prevalent in coastal communities.

■ **One way to reduce the vulnerability of coastal populations is to adopt disaster-related policies and practices that better reflect an understanding of the daily circumstances of families. Rigid definitions of what constitutes a family should be avoided when qualifying families for assistance. Effective family services include child care at disaster application centers; outreach programs for those without private transportation; policies to facilitate kinship networks of assistance; and programs to deal with family stress, conflict, and violence. A major step toward improving services to families, and improving disaster response in general, would be to use the resources of the nation's women more effectively at all levels of disaster planning and response. This includes hiring and including more women at decision-making levels in emergency management and disaster response planning and creating participatory processes to help build inclusiveness of gender, age, race, and those with disabilities into consensus-building public meetings, discussions, and workshops related to mitigation and disaster response.**

In summary, the human community turns a hazard into a disaster. As the coasts become increasingly populated, more and more people are placed in harm's way. Thus far, science has not found effective ways to reduce most hazards. Therefore, citizens must look to strengthening communities. Building safer buildings and infrastructure are important steps, but it is the manner in which *societies* are built that largely determines disaster resilience. A vital part of effective disaster planning—whether for mitigation, preparation, response, or recovery—is an understanding of the people and institutions that make up each community, including their strengths and their weaknesses, as a basis for developing policies, programs, and practices to protect them. In the end, it is human decisions on such matters as land use planning and community priorities that will ultimately build stronger, safer, and better communities.

1

INTRODUCTION AND BACKGROUND

THROUGHOUT HUMAN HISTORY, people have formed settlements along the nation's coastlines. Whether for food, livelihood, transport, recreation, or ambiance, humans choose to live where the sea meets the land. This choice does not come without risk. This study by The H. John Heinz III Center for Science, Economics and the Environment explores the relationship between human coastal settlement patterns and the social vulnerability of these communities, including impacts of coastal disasters on individuals and institutions.

Other reports related to coastal vulnerability have analyzed and gathered data on the disaster-related costs of coastal development—both the financial resources needed to repair damaged infrastructure, and the direct, quantifiable insured losses from disasters. An earlier report by The Heinz Center (2000b) explored the categories of what the study panel termed "hidden costs" of coastal hazards. That report concluded that the total costs of coastal hazards far exceed current estimates and provided further evidence of the need for mitigation to lessen vulnerability. These hidden costs include not only the losses to the built environment, but also impacts such as uninsured business interruption costs, social and family disruptions and health costs, and costs of the damages to natural resources and ecosystem services. The current study reaches beyond the economic impacts of disasters on the built environment to explore the inherent risk to people living along the coasts and to the communities they create.

SCOPE OF WORK

Following the release of *The Hidden Costs of Coastal Hazards* report in October 2000, discussions were held with the National Oceanic and

Atmospheric Administration (NOAA) Coastal Services Center staff about a follow-up study based on the recommendations. A decision was made to address the human and social vulnerability aspects of natural coastal disasters in the next project. Human vulnerability—or those circumstances that place people at risk while reducing their means of response or denying them protection—is an integral concern in the development and evaluation of disaster policies (Comfort et al. 1999). For many reasons, including the escalating costs of disaster response, traditional policies that rely only on sending assistance after a disaster must be changed. A new national emphasis on mitigation strategies has emerged. To that end, this study is directed toward the goal of achieving more disaster-resilient coastal communities, beginning at the level of individual households and neighborhoods. Building upon the framework for community planning developed in the Hidden Costs study, the present investigation covers new ground by focusing on the social construct of vulnerability, including how human alteration of the land largely contributes to the impacts of natural disasters. Areas of concern in this study are the human vulnerability of coastal communities, with an emphasis on the identification of high-risk populations; the human impacts of disasters, including the mental and physical health effects on individuals; and the impacts of natural hazards on the social institutions that make up coastal communities. Human vulnerability is created in part by the ways in which coastal communities are developed and managed. Therefore, this report provides a series of recommendations for programs and policies involving all levels of government, community-based organizations, the private sector, and individual households designed to mitigate the effects of the natural hazard risk that is inherent in coastal communities.

BIOGEOGRAPHY OF THE COAST

The coastal environments of the United States are extremely diverse in their biological and geological characteristics. From the ice floes of North Alaska to the rocky headlands of Maine, from the vast marshes of the Gulf of Mexico to the coral reefs of Florida and Hawaii, each coastal region has its own unique features. However, two features—a constantly moving sea and ocean-generated weather—are common to all these areas.

The coastal United States is home not only to people, but also to a rich and diverse set of flora and fauna. Some 95,000 miles of the

U.S. coastline encompasses 15,000 square miles of coastal wetlands and 2,500 square miles of developed barrier islands (National Oceanic and Atmospheric Administration 1998). If people and their houses and infrastructure were not present in these coastal environments, the flora and fauna would move, change, and adapt to the natural forces of the coast. However, human developments make the impacts of natural, weather-related, and other hazards much worse. Development of the land in coastal areas alters patterns of biota significantly through changes in natural systems and the proliferation of introduced flora and fauna. Coastal areas are also home to marine fishes and other marine flora and fauna important to humans, wildlife, and the natural environment. For example, over 80 percent of the commercially valuable marine fishes on the U.S. East Coast spend part of their life cycle in the Albemarle-Pamlico Sound behind the Outer Banks of North Carolina, a habitat increasingly being degraded by human impacts (Albemarle-Pamlico Estuarine Study 1994).

The physical effects on coastal areas include storm surge flooding, storm-driven waves, erosion, wind, rain, earthquakes, tsunamis, and sea level rise (Heinz Center 2000b). Another geological feature of some coastal areas, particularly in California and Alaska, is the presence of fault lines in the earth's crust, making these areas also at risk for earthquakes.

STORMS, SEA LEVEL RISE, AND COASTAL EROSION

Storm systems, often hundreds of miles in diameter, reach miles into the atmosphere and achieve wind speeds of between 100 and 200 miles per hour. Their strength is gained from the thermal effect of warm ocean waters, and they most often dissipate once they reach land. During the last century, more than 170 hurricanes have made landfall in the United States (Elsner and Kara 1999). However, the number and intensity of hurricanes during any single season is highly variable and coincides with the El Niño/La Niña cycle (Pielke and Landsea 1999). For example, during the 1975–1998 period, 82 hurricanes made landfall in the United States, causing nearly 400 fatalities, more than 4,000 injuries, and more than $75 billion in direct losses (Cutter 2001). Although 1985 was a peak year in terms of landfalling hurricanes (eight), the number of injuries was highest in 1989 (five storms), and the value of losses was highest in 1992, with Hurricane Andrew (and three other hurricanes). Unfortunately, it

Figure 1.1 In October 1991, thousands of residents of Monmouth Beach, New Jersey, were threatened by a northeaster. Photo courtesy of the U.S. Army Corps of Engineers.

does not take a hurricane to affect a coastline significantly; negative impacts also can be experienced from a constant wind force from one direction, such as a northeaster on the East Coast (Figure 1.1).

Using historic hurricane data, Jagger et al. (2001) developed a dynamic probability model of hurricane winds for the Gulf and Atlantic coasts. In any given year, the annual exceedance probability for a Category 1* hurricane ranges from zero to 25 percent. Geographically, the largest annual exceedance values are found in southern Florida, eastern North Carolina, and the central Texas coast (Figure 1.2)

Sea level rise will affect virtually every coast in the world (Leatherman et al. 2000). Humans have placed large amounts of infrastructure in coastal areas, many of which are in low-lying regions (the

---

* The Saffir–Simpson Scale ranks hurricanes using a category system of 1–5. Category 1: winds are 74–95 mph and damage is minimal. Category 2: winds are 96–110 mph and damage is moderate. Category 3: winds are 111–130 mph and damage is extensive. Category 4: winds are 131–155 mph and damage is extreme. In Category 5 storms, winds are more than 155 mph and damage is catastrophic.

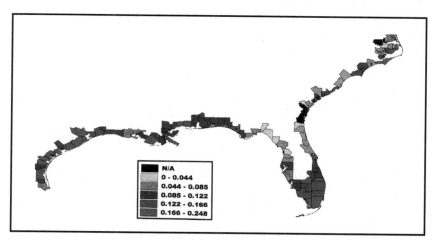

Figure 1.2 Annual exceedance probabilites for Category 1 hurricanes are highest in the southeastern states. Reprinted with permission from Jagger et al. 2001.

city of New Orleans, for example, is below mean sea level and is kept dry by a system of drains and pumps). In fact, 14 of the 20 largest U.S. cities are located in coastal zones (National Oceanic and Atmospheric Administration 1998a). These cities on the coast present special problems related to natural hazards and sea level rise because of the high density of human habitation and large amount of infrastructure involved. Cities depend on the functioning and interaction of complex social, political, and engineering systems, all of which are vulnerable to disruption by a natural hazard (Institute for Business and Home Safety 2001). The rising sea level, in combination with large storms, flooding, and powerful ocean waves, is driving erosion, which is wearing away the beaches and bluffs along the U.S. ocean and Great Lakes shorelines. Erosion undermines waterfront homes, businesses, and public infrastructure, eventually making them uninhabitable or unusable. As the shoreline moves inland, erosion also brings nearby structures ever closer to the water, often putting them at greater risk than either their owners or insurers expected (Heinz Center 2000a). Over the next 60 years, erosion may claim one out of four houses within 500 feet of the U.S. shoreline. To the people living and working within this area, the risk posed by erosion is comparable to the risk from flooding, especially in beach areas (Heinz Center 2000a).

EARTHQUAKES

The Pacific coastal states (California, Oregon, Washington, Alaska, and Hawaii) are among the most tectonically active regions in the world. In California, the juxtaposition of known earthquake faults and high population densities in coastal counties increases the risk for these communities. The potential for ground shaking, slope failure, land subsidence, liquefaction, and tsunamis can compound coastal processes, making these environments and the people and wildlife living there very vulnerable. The combination of natural (e.g. earthquakes, storms, hurricanes) and technological hazards creates an environment in which effects may be multiplied through cascading multidisasters. For instance, a severe earthquake might, in some countries, lead to a breakdown in the social order and infrastructure, resulting in rioting, the spread of disease through unsafe drinking water, and disruptions to the local economy (Institute for Business and Home Safety 2001).

The Federal Emergency Management Agency (FEMA) (2001c) estimated that the earthquake loss to the national building stock averages $4.4 billion per year. This figure includes the estimated long-term value of building stock, including repair and replacement costs for structural and nonstructural components, building content loss, business inventory loss, and income losses. Annual losses are concentrated in West Coast counties (84 percent), with the majority of those losses in California ($3.3 billion), especially in coastal counties. Annualized earthquake loss is $500 million for all coastal counties from San Diego in the south to Whatcom County, Washington, in the north. In Alaska and Hawaii, the annualized earthquake loss ranges from $100 million or more in most coastal counties (Figure 1.3).

Earthquake losses are escalating. The October 1989 Loma Prieta earthquake produced nearly $5 billion in losses (Cutter 2001). The recorded costs associated with the 1994 Northridge earthquake exceed $24 billion; if uninsured losses are added, the total is estimated to be about $44 billion (Eguchi et al. 1996). Given the magnitude of these two seismic events, the combined loss of life could have been much worse than the 119 recorded fatalities.

THE COAST: A FRAGILE ECOSYSTEM

Coasts are home to many of America's most valuable ecosystems. Besides the obvious market-based foods and services, such as fisheries and transportation,

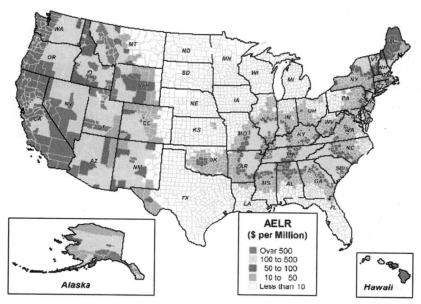

Figure 1.3 Annualized earthquake losses in the United States are highest on the West Coast. *Source*: Federal Emergency Management Agency 2001b.

coastal ecosystems provide humans and wildlife with life-supporting services. Coastal ecosystems also provide biodiversity protection functions, such as wildlife habitat and migration corridors. Ecosystem services of coastal wetlands include the purification of water, mitigation of floods and drought, and generation of fertile soils. As mentioned earlier, erosion of these ecosystems occurs even without major storms because of natural wave action.

Damage to natural ecosystems and resources is inevitable during and after a hurricane, earthquake, or other natural disaster. This damage results in more runoff, floods, and the closing of shellfish beds and beaches because of runoff pollution. Tourism and other industries are affected, and livelihoods may be lost in communities where tourism and recreation are important to the local economy.

Natural disasters take a huge toll on the natural environment and wildlife. For example, during Hurricane Hugo, an estimated 63 percent of the Atlantic Coast's largest population of the endangered red-cockaded woodpecker, located in Francis Marion National Forest, was lost. Many other species, both common and endangered, also were affected. The ranges of five species of endangered or threatened sea turtles include South Carolina's beaches. Sea turtle nesting sites were damaged during the storm, and beach restoration activities after the storm further damaged many areas (Heinz Center 2000b)

Coastal ecosystems provide a variety of "free" goods and services that are used and valued by human society but are often hidden in economic analyses. In coastal areas, these services could include the storm buffering provided by beaches and dunes, as well as floodwater storage by wetlands. According to Costanza et al. (1997), the current economic value of 17 ecosystem services for 16 biomes is extremely high. Although Costanza's estimates for ecosystem services are controversial, few dispute the vital contributions of coastal ecosystems to the sustainability of modern society (Heinz Center 2000b). Society's success in protecting important habitats and species depends not only on the day-to-day impacts on them, but also on humans' ability to make responsible decisions over the long term. Development strategies that contribute to the decline or even extinction of species result in significant losses to human societies.

People living in coastal communities are economically and culturally dependent on, and often emotionally linked to, the natural environment. Indeed, human survival in many coastal communities is directly dependent upon, and linked to, natural resources. Thus, when disasters strike, not only are the physical and natural environments affected, but so too is the human dependence upon them. Knowledge of how coastal environments function and interact with their inhabitants is becoming ever more crucial in the effort to improve mitigation of and response to coastal hazards.

HUMAN USE OF THE COAST

Historically, people have occupied coastal areas primarily for economic reasons. Many important industries are located in coastal areas, including fisheries, agriculture, silviculture, marine transportation, and tourism services. Indeed, the first U.S. cities and areas of human settlement were on the coasts, and most of the major cities to this day are port cities, including those on the Great Lakes.

The marine fishing industry, one of the oldest industries in the nation, remains both economically and culturally significant. This is also true for marine recreational fishing, the constituency for which resides both within and outside coastal areas. Jobs associated with this industry range from boat building and repair to fishing, product packaging, and fisheries management.

Rich agricultural soils along the coasts and the convenient transportation of goods contribute to agricultural economies. Livestock rearing and crop cultivation are common coastal industries, employing many and providing the basis for much of the country's food supply.

Marine ports are an integral part of the nation's economy, bringing in goods on as many as 42,000 vessels annually, and providing thousands of jobs. In 1996, 41 percent of the value of U.S. foreign trade, and a much higher percentage by weight, was carried on the ocean, compared to 27 percent by air and 31 percent over land (National Oceanic and Atmospheric Administration 1998). Similarly, the military has made significant use of coastal and marine environments for both offensive and defensive purposes (Wenk 1972).

Economics and culture come together in leisure, tourism, and the retirement industry. Leisure is now the largest industry in the world and is becoming the largest industry on many U.S. coastlines (Miller and Auyong 1991). A phenomenon known as the "gentrification of the coast" (Johnson and Orbach 1991) is causing the replacement of many traditional coastal industries with leisure, tourism, and retirement-oriented businesses.

The beaches are a special attraction, providing not only an economic engine, but also an important opportunity for relaxation and regeneration. Beaches are the number one vacation spot for Americans, according to a recent poll (National Oceanic and Atmospheric Administration 2001). This contributes to development trends, such as beach houses built and purchased for entrepreneurial or investment purposes. Along some coastlines in the United States, an extensive tourism and recreation industry has sprung up, including snorkeling, scuba diving, surfing, whale watching, and more. In addition, recreational boating unrelated to fishing is a popular activity. The nation's oldest historic areas are popular tourist attractions, and many of these areas are located on the coasts because of colonial settlement patterns.

Coastal development also has become a lucrative economic force for private investors. The deluge of people living on and near the coasts is not merely a fad that soon will yield to a preference for inland locations. It is largely a result of population growth combined with the beauty and economic promise of coastal areas. This growing interest in coastal development, combined with a strong economy, in recent years has increased the pressure on landowners to sell or develop.

Not to be forgotten, the coast remains an area where many people engage in some form of subsistence activity (defined as direct consumption of a product without that product entering the market system). For example, subsistence fishing takes place in coastal areas and is especially common among Alaska's native tribes as a means of supplying their villages with large amounts of fish protein. Similarly, subsistence farming is common in coastal areas, often in the form of household gardens or farm plots worked in concert with some form of wage-earning activity. The loss of such products and services because of coastal hazards is left completely out of most disaster impact analyses.

In summary, coastal regions are dominated by all manner of human activity. The natural environment is linked inextricably with social and ecological components. Society has been struggling to meet the needs of an ever-increasing human population with minimal harm to natural ecosystems, land and water quality, and biodiversity.

As stated by Brunckhorst and Bridgewater (1996), the management of land and sea requires teamwork based on a continually evolving consensus on the direction towards sustainable integrated resource management. However, examples of holistic goal setting, or any kind of collective decision making or networked partnering, are rare. It is quite difficult for traditional local, state, and federal governmental entities to deal constructively with the scale, complexity, and interrelatedness of social and environmental problems for the long-term sustainability of coastal regions.

COASTAL POPULATION CHANGES

Under the NOAA definition, 670 of the nation's 3,111 counties are coastal counties, with at least 15 percent of their land area in either a coastal watershed or a coastal cataloging unit (U.S. Bureau of the Census 1995). Although accounting for only 17 percent of the land area of the conterminous United States, these counties are home to 53 percent of the population (National Oceanic and Atmospheric Administration 1998). Urbanization and increasing population pressures have enveloped coastal counties over the last century.

In 1900, for example, there were 11 million people living in the counties bordering the Gulf and Atlantic coasts (Figure 1.4). By 1950, these same counties had experienced a 136 percent increase in population, and by 2000, the population had doubled again (105 percent increase), with 53 million people living in these coastal counties.

Intensified development along the nation's coasts continues to place ever more property and people at risk from weather-related hazards, earthquakes, and landslides. The coastal population density per square mile was 187 in 1960 and 273 in 1994, and it is expected to reach 327 by 2015 (National Oceanic and Atmospheric Administration 1998). Coastal regions experiencing especially high growth rates are California (Los Angeles and San Diego counties); the Houston, Texas, region (Harris County); and South Florida. Coastal cities such as Miami and Fort Lauderdale are poised for even more growth in the future. From a 1990 population of about 9 million, the Miami/Fort Lauderdale region is expected to grow to between 15 million and 30 million people by 2050.

While the population has increased dramatically, the value of insured property along the coasts has increased at an even faster rate. In many of the most popular areas, high-rise buildings hug the coastline (Figure 1.5)

The way in which development occurs—the human use of the land—determines in part the extent to which people, property, and the natural environment are affected. The sociopolitical environment in which decisions related to land use planning and practices are made, the establishment and enforcement of building codes, community preparedness, evacuation, and other hazard-related activities ultimately affect the extent to which the people living in a particular region are at risk.

HUMAN VULNERABILITY

To create better mitigation strategies, emergency response, and land use planning, decision makers at all levels need help in defining risk and vulnerability. The Heinz Center's *Hidden Costs* report emphasized the importance of accurate risk assessment as a basis for developing programs and policies to reduce societal and environmental exposure to natural hazard impacts (Heinz Center 2000b). The report recommended a more comprehensive view of risk assessment, moving beyond conventional methods to include measures of social vulnerability. Based on these recommendations,

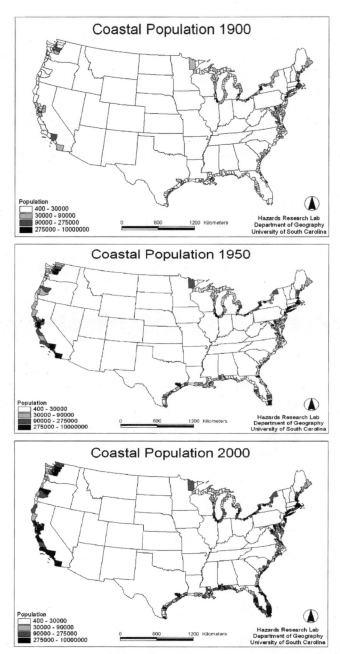

Figure 1.4 From 1900 to 2000, coastal counties experienced a fivefold increase in population. *Source*: University of South Carolina, Hazards Research Lab.

Figure 1.5 Miami Beach is an example of a highly developed shoreline. *Source*: Ron Francis, City of Miami Beach.

the study panel for the present report developed a framework of social vulnerability (see Chapter 2). This report provides a table of population characteristics influencing social vulnerability (Table 2.2, page 44) to help communities identify, locate, and map high-risk groups that may be especially vulnerable to the effects of coastal natural hazards. It is not enough to know who is at risk, but such information can help planners to understand better the nature of that risk. This report also provides evidence of the specific ways in which individuals and social institutions can be affected. Achieving a better understanding of the extent and nature of social vulnerability is an important first step toward developing communities that are more disaster-resilient.

Most disaster losses do not stem from unexpected events. They are the predictable results of interactions among the biophysical environment, the social and demographic characteristics of the communities that experience them, and the built environment. It is increasingly clear that the problems associated with natural hazards—like those associated with the terrorism of September 11, 2001—cannot be solved in isolation, but rather are symptoms of broader, more basic social and political issues. The practice of vulnerability analysis has shifted from an emphasis on nature as the cause of disasters toward an understanding of the role that humans play in creating vulnerability (Anderson 2000).

As Donald Kennedy, the editor of *Science*, wrote in 2002:

Science can play a role in helping with prevention and mitigation as well as recovery and repair. It will make its greatest contribution if we consider our vulnerability to terror attacks and to natural disaster jointly rather than separately. Because our social and economic arrangements have made us vulnerable to both, we can gain from working on them together with a program that involves social sciences as deeply as the natural sciences.

2

HUMAN VULNERABILITY OF COASTAL COMMUNITIES

MANY GLOBAL, NATIONAL, and regional trends and processes influence the production of vulnerability at the local level. Increasing urbanization (especially in hazard-prone areas) has placed more people at risk than ever before. Disparities between rich and poor, continuing racial and ethnic inequities that result in segregation, and more leisure time leading to increased recreational demand on coastal environments are some of the underlying factors that produce current levels of vulnerability. These driving forces affect people and their communities at many different levels, resulting in an uneven landscape of vulnerability from the household to the national level. One big unknown is how these driving forces manifest themselves locally in either constraining or enhancing vulnerability.

This chapter examines the human vulnerability of coastal environments and assesses the magnitude of social impacts driven by changes following a hazard event. In this report, vulnerability is the extent to which natural and social systems, as well as people and their communities, are susceptible to damage from a coastal disaster. Vulnerability depends on the sensitivity of the natural and social system (the degree to which a system will respond to a given hazard event), adaptability (the degree to which adjustments can moderate or offset potential damage), and the degree of exposure to coastal disasters.

A FRAMEWORK FOR ASSESSING VULNERABILITY

When thinking of vulnerability, one immediately is confronted with questions: What type of harm or loss? Who or what is affected? Where is

29

this occurring? In responding to these queries, it is useful to think of three different types of vulnerability: human, built environment, and biophysical. Each has different origins and contextual factors that either restrict or enhance its effect on a particular case or locale (Figure 2.1).

For example, biophysical vulnerability is produced by the interaction between physical processes and human activity and can originate from diverse phenomena such as natural hazards (floods, earthquakes, coastal

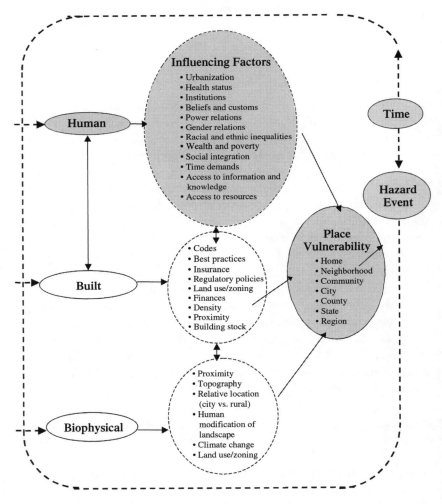

Figure 2.1 Framework for assessing vulnerability. The shaded areas show the focus of this report. Adapted from Cutter 1996.

storms); technological failures (industrial accidents, chemical spills); or more routine and/or chronic environmental threats, such as pollution, coastal erosion, or global warming. The level (or severity) of the biophysical vulnerability can be moderated by a number of factors, such as proximity to the source of the threat, topography of the area, or local land use practices. Similarly, biophysical vulnerability can be increased (and often greatly magnified) through human actions that modify the natural landscape. An example of this is the development of watersheds, which reduces the amount of natural recharge areas (through the paving over of natural areas), which in turn increases runoff and, ultimately, the severity of localized flooding. Overall, residential and recreational development in coastal areas provides another example of actions that increase the biophysical vulnerability to coastal storms (Box 2.1).

The vulnerability of the built environment is a measure of potential economic loss (or exposure) of structures (houses, industries) and infrastructure (highways, bridges, power facilities). The individual susceptibility of buildings and infrastructure to damage from hazardous events is normally an issue restricted to the domain of the engineering sciences. However, there are nonstructural indicators that can be used to assess the overall vulnerability of the built environment; these include local building codes, best engineering practices, insurance, land use, zoning, financing, and regulatory policies. It is also important to note that the density of the built environment, proximity of structures to the source of the hazard (e.g., location in floodplain or on a barrier island), and building stock age and composition also affect the overall vulnerability of the built environment.

The remaining type of vulnerability, human, is the focal point of this chapter. Human vulnerability can be described as those individual characteristics of people (age, gender, race, health, and personal habits) that make them more susceptible to harm from environmental threats. If one moves beyond the individual level to consider households and communities, then there are other factors that contribute to the reduction or enhancement of human vulnerability; such factors include urbanization, racial inequities, poverty, and wealth.

The interactions of human, built-environment, and biophysical vulnerability (along with constraining or enhancing factors) contribute to the overall vulnerability of places (Figure 2.1). Depending on the focus, these places can range from the smallest unit, such as a home, to a neighborhood, city, county, or beyond. If measurements are made in similar ways, one can compare the relative vulnerability of various places to see

Box 2.1   The Hurricane Coast

Florida's history is replete with examples of hurricane-induced storm erosion. With more than 1,000 miles of coastline, its unusual geography, and its location near the tropics, Florida is the number-one pin in the U.S. hurricane bowling alley. Virtually every region of the state has been subjected to storm surge and wave-induced coastal erosion (Barnes 1998). The state's bathymetry and predominantly sandy shoreline subject to high-energy waves combine to ensure that even minor tropical cyclones can cause widespread and sometimes serious coastal damage in many areas. For example, Hurricane Dora (1964) made landfall just north of Saint Augustine as a Category 3 storm. By all accounts, the slow movement of the storm produced record storm surges that destroyed beaches, roadways, and concrete seawalls and swept several dwellings and structures into the sea. The U.S. Coast Guard Station in Volusia County reportedly lost more than 200 feet of beach.

The Florida Keys not only are exposed to the ravages of coastal erosion, but also are faced with utter isolation in every approaching hurricane. The flat chain of coral islands is extremely vulnerable to storm tides and wave action, but U.S. Route 1 (the Overseas Highway), the main roadway that connects the Keys to the mainland, has been severed completely a number of times when its chain of bridges and causeways was broken. In recent history, hurricanes Donna (Category 4 at landfall) and Betsy (Category 3) not only damaged numerous structures in the Florida Keys, but also washed out bridges and consequently severed the only source of potable water for many residents. Hurricane Donna is also credited with destroying one of the largest remaining stands of big mangrove trees that was not destroyed by the 1935 Labor Day storm that caused widespread fatalities in the Keys.

Many storms that have caused serious coastal erosion in Florida have not even made landfall. Hurricanes David and Frederic in 1979, and Hurricane Elena in 1985, visited widespread coastal damage on both the Atlantic and Panhandle coastlines (i.e., beach erosion was severe, high seas undermined numerous seawalls, and causeways and bridges along the entire western coastline were destroyed).

where the burdens (social and structural) are greatest, and where the risks (biophysical) are greatest.

Vulnerability can be reduced through a variety of mechanisms, such as those listed in the middle of Figure 2.1 and described later in this chapter. Finally, it should be noted that the entire vulnerability framework can change over time (based on changes in any of its components) or in response to a single hazard event (such as the Northridge earthquake or Hurricane Floyd). In both instances, these changes provide a feedback loop (shown as a dashed line in Figure 2.1) that then modifies the human, built-environment, and/or biophysical vulnerability, and the cycle continues. Box 2.2 describes some of the modifications of biophysical vulnerability in the Florida Panhandle following Hurricane Opal.

HUMAN FACTORS CONTRIBUTING TO VULNERABILITY

The impact of a coastal hazard, such as a hurricane, affects far more than the biophysical environment. It has the capacity to wreak havoc on the people, social institutions, and networks that make up a community. A community can be thought of as a group of people who not only live in proximity to each other but also are bound together in complex ways to meet their everyday needs. Institutions normally are described as a set of groups and organizations linked through divisions of labor around specific functions, such as education, economics, and governance. Coastal communities are also ecological networks that connect the flow of energy, materials, goods, and services in these regions.

Thinking of today's communities as single systems oversimplifies a complex, often contentious process in which groups with diverse interests and levels of power compete for resources. Indeed, this sociopolitical ecology perspective is especially useful when thinking of coastal hazards because it emphasizes the conflict and competition that largely determines which ideas and interests prevail, including those associated with land use, hazard mitigation, and disaster response (Peacock and Ragsdale 2000). In this sense, a community with a relatively low level of vulnerability is one in which, in addition to good land use and resource management, there is relative social and economic equality, cooperation and understanding among diverse cultural groups, and a well-functioning political system. Mitigation involves far more than the hardening of buildings and infrastructure, extending to a careful examination of a community's social and political milieu. Given this view of a community, assessing the vulnerability and response capability of a specific coastal region requires an understanding of not only its population characteristics and distribution, but also the economic and political systems that largely

Box 2.2 Hurricane Opal: The Little Storm That Could

Hurricane Opal provides a dramatic example of storm-surge-induced coastal erosion. As Hurricane Opal increased speed toward the Florida Panhandle from the Gulf of Mexico, it rapidly intensified from a Category 1 to a Category 4 storm overnight. Florida and Alabama residents and tourists were confronted with the need to evacuate, creating major traffic congestion along virtually every roadway along the Gulf Coast from Florida to Mississippi, and leaving many people stranded on the roads as tropical-storm-force winds approached. Fortunately, before Opal made landfall, dry air became entrained in its circulation and it became a marginally Category 3 storm before landfall on October 4, 1995.

Despite Opal's fortuitous de-intensification, it had invested a great deal of energy in the ocean. For nearly 300 miles of coastline eastward from Mobile, the storm surge was between 4 and 7 feet. The wave heights in some places were 10 feet above normal, and from Navarre Beach to Blue Mountain Beach, the wave heights exceeded 24 feet above mean sea level. The resulting coastal erosion was catastrophic and widespread in this region. Significant losses of dunes (in both height and width) were observed, with many dunes breached or flattened. The retreat of dune faces in several areas approached 75 to 100 feet, and overwash of eroded dune sediments was common, in some cases extending more than 500 feet inland, burying roads and filling structures with up to 4 feet of sand. An

determine how hazard vulnerability is conceptualized and distributed among and between people and places (Box 2.3).

INSTITUTIONAL INVOLVEMENT IN VULNERABILITY

Coastal development patterns are the result of a complex interplay between public and private institutions and actors. The public sector historically has played, and continues to play, an influential role in supporting and facilitating coastal development and growth, and safer buildings and stronger building codes, albeit much of it in risky places and in risky ways.

Government at all levels tends to boost development. Local and state governments are eager to capture the tax base, economic growth, and perceived benefits from reduced tax rates, more jobs, and more income.

Box 2.2 continued

estimated 10 to 20 feet of vertical relief was lost at the seaward edge of some high dune and bluff areas, causing many oceanfront structures to collapse. Opal's power severed mainland access to Saint Joseph Peninsula and Cape San Blas, and required the closure of Saint George Island State Park, more than 125 miles from where the storm made landfall, for over one year to allow time to restore and repair the dunes, roads, and public facilities. Hurricane Opal completely destroyed approximately 3,500 homes and inflicted major damage on another 5,300 structures in Florida, with the estimated losses exceeding $3 billion despite the fact that this storm was not a major hurricane.

Destruction along the Gulf Coast of Florida, October 1995.

Photo by Beau Hannah.
Source: US Army Corps of Engineers, www.fema.gov/hu95/images25.gif.

Local political campaigns frequently center on this issue and are won or lost accordingly.

Numerous local governmental jurisdictions in the U.S. coastal zone face this issue. There are 670 coastal counties across the country in addition to numerous coastal cities and towns. In Florida alone, there are 465 cities and counties, as well as regional entities (e.g., water management districts, regional planning councils), all considered "coastal" under the state's coastal management program. The fragmented nature of local governmental structures and decision-making processes (especially with regard to land use) throughout coastal America is one important reason why coordinated, far-sighted planning and development decisions are difficult to achieve.

In many coastal communities, priority is given to attracting and encouraging growth, with little consideration for long-term environmental damage, loss of quality of life, or social costs that accompany such growth. Because the historical dependence on local property taxes continues

Box 2.3 Disaster-Resilient Communities: Asking the
Right Questions

What is the economic health of the community? Are its businesses stable and its economic base strong? What about its schools and cultural institutions? What health and social services are available and how are they distributed? Is this a stable community or is the population in a state of flux? To what extent are groups bound together by common goals? Social cohesion can reduce disaster vulnerability and dramatically improve a community's ability to respond. What is the level and nature of political participation? How do the various political entities function? Is there a competitive environment among different municipalities? If so, how is power distributed? Is there an active civil society? To what extent are minority views represented throughout?

The disaster resistance of an individual neighborhood or household depends on whether it has the autonomy and resources, including human resources, to respond to a hazard. What are the daily circumstances of people living in this community? What types of residential housing (e.g., single-family homes, mobile homes, apartments) are located where? Do people tend to own their own homes or rent? What is the average household size? What is the average household income? What is the neighborhood's age distribution (i.e., children, elderly)? How far do people commute to work, schools, and stores? Where are the critical facilities that serve the area? To what extent are households connected into networks of social interaction (i.e., extended families, homeowners' associations, sports leagues, religious groups)? Social integration, that is, people bound together in networks of social support, strengthens the ability to respond to a crisis of any type (Morrow 1999).

to this day, attracting increasingly valuable property is a paramount goal for many communities. Coastal counties are especially motivated to capture second-home growth, which requires few traditional public services, such as schools, and helps keep local tax rates low.

The incentive structure for coastal growth is clear. At the same time, a number of public policies also affect development in the coastal zone. These public policies can be categorized as (1) explicit coastal policies, that is, policies aimed directly at the coastal zone or management of the resources found therein, such as the Coastal Zone Management Act (CZMA of 1972, P.L. 92-583); (2) other management laws, policies, and programs, not specifically coastal in nature but seeking to influence planning and management more broadly, such as the Clean Water Act (P.L. 92-500) or the Robert T. Stafford Disaster Relief and Emergency Assistance Act of 1993 (P.L. 103-181); and (3) *de facto* coastal policies, including a wide range of subsidies and investments that often have the unintended effect of promoting coastal development (Beatley et al. 1994). Table 2.1 provides some examples of programs and policies in each category. For a more comprehensive overview of coastal agencies and actors, see Klee (1999) and Beatley et al. (1994). Although the various state and local programs are too numerous to be discussed here, it is important to comment briefly on several federal programs that are among the major drivers of coastal development.

DISASTER RESPONSE AND MITIGATION PROGRAMS

At present, there is no overarching federal policy governing land use and development in high-hazard coastal areas. Instead, there are many laws

Table 2.1 Federal Public Policies Affecting the Coastal Zone

Explicit Coastal Policy
    Coastal Zone Management Act
    Coastal Barrier Resources Act
    Fisheries Conservation and Management Act
    Marine Protection, Research, and Sanctuaries Act
    Oil Pollution Act

Environmental Laws and Programs Affecting the Coast
    Clean Water Act (e.g., Section 404)
    Endangered Species Act
    Conservation Reserve Program
    Resource Conservation and Recovery Act
    Comprehensive Environmental Response, Compensation, and Liability Act
      (Superfund)
    Federal Land Policy and Management Act
    National Environmental Policy Act

De facto Coastal Policy
    Stafford Act (Federal Disaster Assistance)
    National Flood Insurance Program
    Federal tax code

and policies, including 50 laws and executive orders related to hazard management. Many federal, state, and local policies emphasize risk reduction and transfer (i.e., standards, insurance, relief) rather than risk assumption and elimination. Some believe that subsidies built into federal insurance and relief programs may account for increased coastal development in hazard-prone areas. The federal and state governments' top-down approach to dealing with local stakeholders has done little to foster the "local involvement, responsibility, and accountability" called for in the most recent comprehensive review of federal policy (Mileti 1999, Interagency Floodplain Management Review Committee 1994).

The Stafford Disaster Relief and Emergency Assistance Act established a discretionary system enabling the President to declare an area affected by a natural hazard as a federal disaster area. The federal disaster designation makes the affected state and declared counties eligible for federal assistance. Platt (1999) notes that the current system encourages states to seek the maximum amount of available disaster resources, irrespective of actual need, and may even contribute to the reluctance of state and local governments to take mitigation actions, such as enacting building codes or enforcing land use regulations.

There is little doubt that the cost of disasters, including coastal disasters, has been increasing for decades and that the share of these costs assumed at the federal level has been rising dramatically as well. Since the 1950s, the average annual number of disaster declarations has tripled (peaking at 75 in 1996). Between 1976 and 2000, there were 861 major disaster declarations, an average of 34 per year (Federal Emergency Management Agency 2001d). Total damage losses from 1975 to 1998 were $500 billion (in 1994 dollars) (Mileti 1999). To be sure, the increasing availability of federal disaster monies may have helped fuel development in coastal areas and discouraged more careful planning and more responsible community growth patterns.

Politics is inextricably linked to all community decisions, particularly those concerning events—such as disasters—that force society to struggle with issues of loss, priorities, and blame (Olson 2000). In a study of the California floods of 1995, Sylves (1996) tested a series of hypotheses to determine what triggers presidential disaster declarations. He concluded that these declarations tend to be issued from the "top down" as a result of political responsiveness to media pressure imposed on the President, rather than issued in a data-driven fashion from the "bottom up" and in accord with established procedures. The public often expects and/or needs a quick response, and the government attempts to respond accordingly. The lack of guidelines defining the basis for declarations results in a process that is perceived to be subject to political pressure—often disproportional to the damages incurred. The number of declarations has been increasing in the last decades, and some suggest that presidents may be using the discretionary disaster declaration authority for political rather than disaster recovery ends (Downton and Pielke 2001, Platt 1999). On the other hand, people hit hard by a natural disaster expect immediate action from their elected representatives; disasters create serious emergencies that must be dealt with quickly.

At the heart of the increasing federalization of disaster response is a cultural shift in how individuals view their own choices, responsibilities, and investment decisions. Knowledge that federal disaster assistance monies will be available to rebuild roads is likely to reduce the incentive to locate and design them in ways that reduce exposure. Actions taken by all levels of government to control disaster management, affix culpability, and influence the flow of disaster funds have tended to move hazard mitigation away from the context of rational planning and technical engineering solutions.

NATIONAL FLOOD INSURANCE PROGRAM

The National Flood Insurance Program (NFIP) was originally designed to minimize the outlay of taxpayer funds in coastal areas where natural hazards are most common. The premise was that, because hazards are expected, an insurance program under which residents pay premiums into a fund will provide a source of revenue to pay for damages when disasters occur. To reduce future losses, the NFIP includes building standards and floodplain management requirements.

For a number of reasons, including the overly low, non-actuarial premiums paid by many homeowners, the program facilitates settlement in areas that are particularly vulnerable to storms. The knowledge that damages will be covered by the NFIP allows people to make investments that they might not otherwise make. Even in instances in which private insurance might have been an option in the absence of federal insurance, the price of private coverage likely would have been actuarial, if not higher, and hence the federal insurance is essentially subsidized. Therefore, by providing less expensive insurance backed by the federal taxpayer, some believe that the NFIP actually encourages coastal development, putting additional lives and property at risk (Platt 1999).

In its earlier study of erosion hazards, The Heinz Center estimated that the density of structures built in high-hazard coastal areas is 15 percent higher than it would have been if the NFIP had not been adopted (Heinz Center 2000a). However, building standards adopted since 1980 have reduced flood and erosion damage per structure by roughly 35 percent (Heinz Center 2000a). Although overall damage is increasing, the rate of damage is lower than it would have been without the program.

One of the most significant challenges facing the NFIP is dealing with homes that have been repeatedly damaged by floods. Some properties have received multiple damage payouts over the years, even as many as a dozen repetitive losses, exceeding the value of the homes. According to the National Wildlife Federation's study *Higher Ground*, a very small number of high-risk properties account for a large portion of flood insurance claims. Specifically, some 40 percent of claims are attributed to just 2 percent of NFIP policyholders (National Wildlife Federation 2000). The NFIP estimates that insured repetitive-loss properties drain the NFIP of $200 million per year (Howard 1999). Of the 300 communities found to have the highest number of repetitive loss properties, coastal communities appear to be disproportionately represented.

CAPITAL IMPROVEMENT PROGRAMS

Capital improvement programs such as beach nourishment, undertaken by the U.S. Army Corps of Engineers (USACE), provide additional stimulation for growth in coastal areas. It is estimated, for example, that more than $1 billion in federal money has been provided for renourishment of beaches (Duke University Program for the Study of Developed Shorelines, Beach Nourishment Database 2002). It is also estimated that the cost of maintaining nourished beaches during the next decade will range from $3.3 million to $17.5 million per mile (Ocean and Coastal Resource Management Program Policy Series 2000). For prospective purchasers of beachfront homes, the value of a home clearly hinges in large part on the presence of the beach. Moreover, a wider beach affords protection against erosion. Although most purchasers are aware that the beach is a dynamic environment that may wash away, the perception that the government will rebuild the beach is a major draw, facilitating development that might not otherwise occur (Dean 1999, Platt 1999).

The federal government's investment in capital improvements in coastal environments goes way beyond beach nourishment. In all, the federal government invests in beachfront development through about 40 programs, including some that are not specific to the beaches. For example, federal highway dollars often are invested to build—and rebuild—highways on barrier islands and in other coastal areas. Federal funds for sewage treatment and drinking water infrastructure also aid the development of these areas.

These capital improvements often are made possible by the aggressive efforts of congressional representatives from coastal states and districts to secure funding for a variety of infrastructure and growth-inducing projects, from new highways to flood control to beach re-nourishment. Often, these projects are supported by a specific member of Congress and his or her local constituents, but not necessarily by the federal agency in charge of implementing and administering the politically mandated "pork barrel" project.

Highway and transportation investments, decisions that are made at the state level but often receive considerable federal funding, are especially important growth shapers. Numerous examples demonstrate the impact of highway construction on growth, including Interstate 40 linking central North Carolina with Wilmington and the beach communities. In general, the exposure of people and property to flooding has been enhanced by federal financing of highway construction, sewers, and other infrastructure that serves to increase the development of flood-prone areas while also reducing development costs (Mileti 1999).

The relatively short electoral cycle encourages elected representatives to seek projects that show physical results and tangible benefits for the community. A replenished beach, for example, can be seen, enjoyed, and touched, offering more political rewards than intangible accomplishments such as good coastal planning and long-term mitigation projects.

COASTAL ZONE MANAGEMENT

Virtually every coastal state participates in the federal Coastal Zone Management Program and has a state agency or office working to implement coastal regulations and management. Often, however, the legal and political powers of such agencies are limited, and the best that can be accomplished is modest mitigation of coastal threats and limited influence on development in the ecologically sensitive and hazard-prone coastal environment. Under the CZMA, state coastal programs are given broad guidance and standards, and each state is left to determine the exact management, legal, and institutional framework that works best. This programmatic approach results in differences among the states, largely based on individual political circumstances.

The different missions and structures of federal agencies involved in coastal affairs often cause these agencies to work at cross-purposes. While NOAA seeks to promote coastal conservation and coastal development patterns to avoid hazards, the USACE provides support and funding for re-nourishment and hurricane protection that allays public concerns about risks, and FEMA (through the NFIP) underwrites the personal risks associated with decisions to build on the coast.

Recognizing these conflicts—and to save taxpayer dollars, save lives, and protect the environment—Congress in 1982 passed the Coastal Barrier Resources Act (P.L. 97-438), which ultimately designated 1.3 million acres of coastal barrier island land for which none of these federal value-added programs would be available. In retrospect, this Act provided the basis for a useful experiment to determine whether these federal investments actually facilitate development that otherwise might not occur. Nearly 20 years after the law was passed, Godschalk and Salveson (undated) examined the effect of federal programs, or their absence, on development. The study showed that, although local governments can step in to facilitate coastal development, areas that are not eligible for federal value-added programs are developed much more slowly than other areas, if developed at all.

TAX INCENTIVES

Low-interest loans and other financial tools serve to help people invest in, and live on, the coasts. In terms of hidden subsidies and inducements, the U.S. tax code is actually a primary form of *de facto* coastal policy. A number of provisions can be seen as subsidies for high-risk coastal growth. The casualty loss deduction, for example, allows coastal homeowners to deduct a portion of the losses experienced from coastal storm damage, in essence rewarding, or at least subsidizing, risky home or investment decisions.

Perhaps most significant has been the ability of those who own second homes on the coast to deduct mortgage interest and local property taxes from their federal income taxes. This provision has served to put a second home within the financial reach of many Americans. They live a portion of the year there and gain rental income the rest of the time. Real estate companies in places such as the Outer Banks of North Carolina aggressively market the benefits of second home investments—a renter one year is encouraged to become an investor and coastal property owner the next.

Tax code treatment of rental properties further exacerbates these pressures. Generous deductions are allowed for maintenance and other business expenses for these properties. In some very significant ways, the U.S. tax code has fueled coastal growth. Potential residents, property owners, and investors in coastal zones are in large part simply responding to these economic signals, incentives, and financial supports.

SOCIAL AND ECONOMIC VULNERABILITY

In coming to grips with first understanding and then measuring vulnerability, one is faced with a complex assessment of which factors exacerbate human vulnerability and which ones moderate it. Take wealth, for example. Wealthier communities (measured by per capita income, housing values, or some other indicator) have more economic investment at potential risk. At the same time, personal wealth enables individuals and communities to absorb losses in ways that poorer communities cannot. There is more opportunity in wealthier places to acquire insurance (or be self-insured), to implement mitigation measures that may improve the structural performance of buildings and infrastructure, or to insist on strengthening land use regulations or building codes. So, does wealth retard or increase the social vulnerability of communities?

Most experts agree that higher density of development, housing tenancy (renting versus owning), and certain types of housing stock (mobile homes and high-rise buildings versus single-family, detached homes) increase vulnerability to coastal hazards. Similarly, there is a consensus that certain social and economic conditions tend to marginalize some categories of people, thus increasing their social vulnerability (Morrow 1999, Bolin and Stanford 1998, Peacock et al. 2000). Table 2.2 summarizes population characteristics that influence the social vulnerability of

TABLE 2.2 Population Characteristics Influencing Social Vulnerability

Population Characteristic	Description	Increases (+) or Decreases (−) Social Vulnerability
Socioeconomic status (income, political power, prestige)	Status affects the ability to absorb losses and enhance resilience to hazard impacts. Wealth enables communities to absorb and recover from losses more quickly using insurance, social safety nets, and entitlement programs.	High status (+/−) Low income or status (+) (*Sources:* Cutter et al. 2000, Peacock et al. 2000, Puente 1999, Bolin and Stanford 1998, Blaikie et al. 1994, Burton et al. 1993)
Gender	Women often have a more difficult time during recovery than men because of sector-specific employment (e.g., personal services), lower wages, and family care responsibilities.	Gender (+) (*Sources:* Peacock et al. 2000, Enarson and Scanlon 1999, Morrow and Phillips 1999, Enarson and Morrow 1998, Hewitt 1997, Fothergill 1996, Morrow and Enarson 1996)
Race and ethnicity	These factors impose language and cultural barriers and affect access to post-disaster funding and occupation of high-hazard areas.	Non-white (+) Non-Anglo (+) (*Sources:* Pulido 2000, Peacock et al. 2000, Morrow and Phillips 1999, Bolin and Stanford 1998, Bolin 1993)
Age	Extremes of age affect the movement out of harm's way. Parents lose time and money caring for children when day care facilities are affected; the elderly may have mobility constraints or concerns that increase the burden of care and lack of resilience.	Elderly (+) Children (+) (*Sources:* Ngo 2001, Cutter et al. 2000, Hewitt 1997, O'Brien and Mileti 1992)
Commercial and industrial development	The value, quality, and density of commercial and industrial buildings provide indicators of the state of economic health of a community, potential losses in the business community, and longer-term issues with recovery after an event.	High density (+) High value (+/−) (*Sources:* Heinz Center 2000b, Webb et al. 2000)

Employment loss	The potential loss of additional employment following a disaster increases the possible number of unemployed workers in a community. Such losses contribute to a slower recovery from the disaster.	Employment loss (+) (Source: Mileti 1999)
Rural/urban	Rural residents may be more vulnerable because of lower incomes and more dependence on a locally based resource economy (e.g., farming or fishing). High-density areas (urban) complicate evacuation out of harm's way.	Rural (+) Urban (+) (Sources: Cutter et al. 2000, Cova and Church 1997)
Residential property	The value, quality, and density of residential construction affect potential losses and recovery. Expensive homes on the coast are costly to replace; mobile homes are easily destroyed and less resilient to hazards.	Mobile homes (+) (Sources: Cutter et al. 2000, Heinz Center 2000b, Bolin and Stanford 1991)
Infrastructure and lifelines	The loss of sewer, bridges, water, communications, and transportation infrastructure compounds potential disaster losses. The loss of infrastructure may place an insurmountable financial burden on smaller communities that lack the financial resources to rebuild.	Extensive infrastructure (+) (Sources: Heinz Center 2000b, Platt 1995)
Renters	People rent because they are transients, do not have the financial resources for home ownership, or do not want the responsibility of home ownership. They often lack access to information about financial aid during recovery. In extreme cases, renters lack sufficient shelter options when lodging becomes uninhabitable or too costly to afford.	Renters (+) (Sources: Heinz Center 2000b, Morrow 1999)

(continued)

TABLE 2.2 *Continued*

Population Characteristic	Description	Increases (+) or Decreases (−) Social Vulnerability
Occupation	Some occupations, especially those involving resource extraction, may be severely affected by a hazard event. Self-employed fishermen suffer when their means of production is lost, and they may not have the requisite capital to resume work in a timely fashion; therefore, they may seek alternative employment. Migrant workers engaged in agriculture and low-skilled service jobs (housekeeping, child care, and gardening) may suffer similarly as disposable income fades and the need for services declines. Immigration status also affects occupational recovery.	Professional or managerial (−) Clerical or laborer (+) Service sector (+) (*Sources*: Heinz Center 2000b, Puente 1999, Hewitt 1997)
Family structure	Families with large numbers of dependents and single-parent households often have limited wherewithal to outsource care for dependents and thus must juggle work responsibilities and care for family members. All these factors affect resilience to and recovery from hazards.	High birth rates (+) Large families (+) Single-parent households (+) (*Sources*: Heinz Center 2000b, Morrow 1999, Puente 1999, Morrow 1997, Blaikie et al. 1994)
Education	Education is linked to socioeconomic status in that higher educational attainment affects lifetime earnings, and limited education constrains the ability to understand warning information and access recovery information.	Little education (+) Highly educated (−) (*Source*: Heinz Center 2000b)
Population growth	Counties experiencing rapid growth lack available high-quality housing, and the social services network may not have had time to adjust to increased populations. New	Rapid growth (+) (*Sources*: Cutter et al 2000, Heinz Center 2000b, Morrow 1999, Puente 1999)

	migrants may not speak the language and may not be familiar with how to deal with bureaucracies in obtaining relief or recovery information. All these factors increase vulnerability.	
Health status	The public health literature shows that people with preexisting illnesses may be at risk for death/illness/injury in disaster settings. People with preexisting cardiovascular and respiratory conditions who are exposed to smoke and haze from forest fires may be more at risk for adverse health outcomes; they also may be vulnerable to heart attacks during seismic activity.	Major health problems (+) Minor or no health problems (−) (Sources: Parati et al. 2001, Brauer 1999, Brown 1999, Minami et al. 1997)
Medical services	Health care providers, including physicians, nursing homes, and hospitals, are important post-event sources of relief. The lack of proximate medical services lengthens the time needed to obtain short-term relief and achieve longer-term recovery from disasters.	Higher density of medical (−) (Sources: Heinz Center 2000b, Morrow 1999, Hewitt 1997)
Social dependence	People who are totally dependent on social services for survival are already economically and socially marginalized and require additional support in the post-disaster period.	High dependence (+) Low dependence (−) (Sources: Heinz Center 2000b, Hewitt 2000, Morrow 1999, Drabek 1996)
Special-needs populations	Special-needs populations (infirm, institutionalized, transient, homeless) are difficult to identify, let alone measure and monitor. Yet it is this segment of society that invariably is left out of recovery efforts, largely because of this invisibility in communities.	Large number of special needs (+) Small number of special needs (−) (Sources: Morrow 1999, Tobin and Ollenburger 1993)

Source: Cutter et al. 2001.

communities in both positive and negative ways. How these social and economic factors influence vulnerability, particularly at the household level, is discussed further in Chapter 3.

The population characteristics associated with social vulnerability are not randomly distributed throughout the United States. Rather, social vulnerability tends to be clustered in pockets of high risk. At both ends of the continuum, rural and urban areas are likely to be home to people who are socially, economically, and politically marginalized. Not surprising, as illustrated in Table 2.3, coastal counties tend to have higher-than-average concentrations of at-risk households.

MEASURING LOCAL VARIABILITY IN VULNERABILITY

In a pilot effort aimed at understanding the underlying dimensions of social vulnerability and its spatial variability, Cutter et al. (2001) created the list of population characteristics influencing social vulnerability (the column on the left in Table 2.2). Using socioeconomic and housing data from the U.S. Census for 1990, the researchers were able to explain slightly more than 80 percent of the variation in vulnerability among all coastal counties in the population characteristics shown in Table 2.2 using a condensed list of eleven dimensions (Table 2.4). This analysis provides much-needed empirical support for the establishment of key indicators of vulnerability, or, in other words, those population characteristics that enhance or constrain the vulnerability of the human and built environments at the local level.

When the factors are summed in a simple additive model, an

Table 2.3 High-Risk Coastal Households in the United States

Group	Percent of Total U.S. Population	Percent in Coastal Counties[a]
Persons 65 or older	12.4	14.0
Black or African American	12.9	16.8
Hispanic or Latino	12.5	14.2
Female-headed households	12.2	13.6
Renter-occupied housing	33.8	36.3

Source: B. Morrow from 2000 Census data.
[a] Includes 178 counties on the Gulf and Atlantic coasts.

Table 2.4   Dimensions of Social Vulnerability on U.S. Coasts

Dimension	Percent of Variation among Counties Explained
Personal wealth and poverty	13.8
Population age structure	13.8
Development of the built environment	12.6
Urban ethnicity	11.6
Gender	5.9
Agricultural	5.5
Native American homelands	4.8
Rapid growth	3.9
Race and unemployment	3.5
Dependent economies	3.4
Infrastructure employment dependence	3.0
TOTAL	81.8

Source: Cutter et al. 2001.

overall composite score or social vulnerability index can be computed for each county. Higher values represent greater relative levels of social vulnerability. Nationally, the top five most socially vulnerable counties are Cameron and Willacy in south Texas; the borough of Manhattan in New York City; San Francisco; and Charles City, Virginia, along the James River (Cutter et al. 2001). Cameron and Willacy counties are notable for poverty, racial mix, age structure, and unemployment characteristics. Manhattan and San Francisco have high values because of extensive development, whereas Charles City has high debt and employment reliance on infrastructure (transportation and utilities).

Mapping of social vulnerability highlights the variability across the nation. Among Gulf Coast and Atlantic coastal counties, greater levels of social vulnerability (higher than the national average) are found in south Texas and the more urbanized counties in Florida. The New York metropolitan region also stands out, as does Los Angeles (Figure 2.2).

PUTTING IT ALL TOGETHER: LOCAL EXPERIENCES

One of the best ways to understand the extent of human vulnerability to coastal hazards is to look at experiences with specific events, the lessons

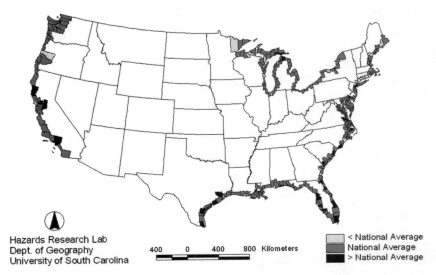

Hazards Research Lab
Dept. of Geography
University of South Carolina

400   0   400   800   Kilometers

< National Average
National Average
> National Average

Figure 2.2 Social vulnerability varies among U.S. coastal counties; the highest values are found in pockets indicated by dark shading on the map. *Source*: Data from the University of South Carolina, Hazards Research Lab, 2002.

learned, and how vulnerability was (or was not) reduced consequently. The remainder of this chapter examines two specific hazard events that altered the vulnerability of different coastal regions, Northern California and eastern North Carolina, focusing on factors associated with special vulnerability.

THE LOMA PRIETA EARTHQUAKE

The Loma Prieta earthquake of October 17, 1989, was the strongest seismic event (magnitude 7.1) to occur in the San Francisco Bay Area since the historic 1906 earthquake. The event, which occurred during the evening rush hour, had an epicenter located near Santa Cruz, California. There were 62 immediate deaths, more than 3,700 injuries, and estimated direct losses exceeding $5 billion (Cutter 2001, Ebert 2000). Two fortuitous factors contributed to a lower injury and fatality rate than otherwise would have been expected given the magnitude of the earthquake: The epicenter was located in an area of relatively low population, and many people were already home and off the freeways because of the World Series baseball game that was being played locally.

The hardest-hit areas included Santa Cruz, which lost most of its downtown business district; the Marina district in San Francisco (built on unconsolidated sediments and fill); and the Oakland flats, where the elevated section of Interstate 880 collapsed and where many of the fatalities occurred (Figure 2.3). Nearly 1,000 homes and 366 businesses were destroyed, and there was damage to an additional 234,000 homes, 1,500 schools, and 3,500 businesses (Ebert 2000). One section of the Bay Bridge collapsed, closing the bridge for a month. Additionally, a couple of small highway overpasses over swamps slumped; a landslide closed Highway 17 for a time until debris was cleared. In some areas such as the Marina, the earthquake interrupted electricity and water for periods of a few weeks to two months. However, mass transit suffered only minor interruptions. The BART system survived undamaged.

Many problems were reported concerning insurance coverage. Lawsuits in the aftermath of the earthquake alleged that major underwriters did not give victims all the help they were due, a charge that one major carrier denied, noting that of more than 27,000 claims totaling $120 million, it had received only 28 complaints. It also was alleged that claims

Figure 2.3 The Cypress Street section of Interstate 880 collapsed in Oakland, California, following the Loma Prieta earthquake. Photo by S. Cutter.

adjusters lacked experience or training, and that damage claims were improperly closed with no or insufficient payment to victims.

Workers' compensation was a major source of damages for injuries and deaths. The concept of workers' compensation is based on liability without fault, and although there are specific limitations on payments (California Labor Code, Section 3600 *et seq.*), "acts of God" are not among them. A more complex workers' compensation issue revolved around the Cypress Street freeway structure and whether employees were commuting from their jobs at the time of their injuries. Although courts have developed the "going-and-coming rule" that excludes workers' compensation coverage for regular commuters, litigation has yet to resolve the question of whether there was a business purpose to some of the victims' trips.

The Loma Prieta earthquake also brought to light another earthquake-related coverage problem. In a then-unpublished decision denying review of an appellate court decision, the California Supreme Court rejected a Mill Valley homeowner's claim that insurance should cover newly required "code upgrades" (*McCorkle v. State Farm Insurance*, August 15, 1990). Although the denial of review did not set a legal precedent, it nonetheless had the effect of requiring the purchase of specific riders because damage payments only cover "equivalent replacement," not restoration in-kind of code updates or restoration of the "historic fabric" of a building.

A year and a half after the Loma Prieta earthquake, many low-income Bay Area residents still were living in homes with leaking roofs and unstable foundations. Many homes had serious structural damage caused by the earthquake that had not yet been repaired. Some community groups and low-income homeowners filed an administrative petition in June 1991. They alleged that the agencies responsible for compensating homeowners for needed repairs (FEMA and the California Department of Social Services' Individual and Family Grant Program) denied low-income homeowners their fair share of relief. The petitioners demanded that an oversight committee review cases to identify people who were not adequately compensated, and asked that additional funds be made available to these groups. The petitioners also requested that policies be changed so that the victims of future disasters would not be subjected to reputedly discriminatory practices (California Seismic Safety Commission 1991).

Another problem centered on media coverage. The initial portrayal of the 1989 Loma Prieta earthquake in the mass media focused on those areas providing the most sensational visual impact, including the Cypress Street section of the I-880 freeway in Oakland (Figure 2.3), a collapsed span of the Bay Bridge, and damage to buildings in the upscale Marina District due to liquefaction and/or fire. Once these pictures were provided to the public, resources and donations poured in, even though these areas were 40 to 50 miles from the earthquake's epicenter. It took a while for national media coverage to focus on the heavily Hispanic areas in and around Watsonville, the college town of Santa Cruz, and the largely African-American city of Oakland. The media's coverage of the Loma Prieta earthquake inadvertently may have created problems in the distribution of critically needed resources, lengthening the recovery process for these residents. This is an excellent example of the sociopolitical dimensions of vulnerability at the community level.

HURRICANE FLOYD

Throughout most of 1999, the Southeast experienced drought conditions. This all changed in September of that year when three storms, hurricanes Dennis, Floyd, and Irene, struck the North Carolina coast, dumping torrential rains during a six-week period. As Hurricane Floyd moved from the Caribbean, its Category 5 strength diminished somewhat as it moved north, taking a path parallel to the southeast coast, first threatening Florida, Georgia, and South Carolina before finally making landfall near Wilmington, North Carolina, as a strong Category 2 hurricane.

Hurricane Floyd was unique in many respects. First, the geographic expanse of the storm and its intensity caught the attention of emergency management workers and the public as the storm first approached the Caribbean and then as it made its way north. The track of the storm meant that residents all along the East Coast were in potential danger from a landfalling hurricane. The combination of the track parallel to the coast, and the sheer size and intensity of the storm, ultimately prompted the largest peacetime evacuation in history, with more than 2 million residents leaving the coast, from Florida to Virginia.

The major evacuation routes in the Southeast (especially Interstate 95) run parallel to the coast. As the storm moved north and skirted Florida, I-95 was packed with evacuees making their way into Georgia, following a path parallel to the storm. Georgians took to the same interstate, creating a wave of traffic jams up and down the East Coast. In

South Carolina, major traffic jams occurred on Interstate 26 out of Charleston as Low Country residents fled the coast. The wave of northward traffic continued into North Carolina on I-95.

When Hurricane Floyd made landfall on September 15, 1999, eastern North Carolina already had experienced another hurricane less than 10 days before. The soils in eastern North Carolina were fairly well saturated after Hurricane Dennis had stalled offshore for many days, and, as it moved onshore, had dumped rainfall amounts ranging from 3 to 7 inches (Bales et al. 2000).

Rainfall totals for Hurricane Floyd in portions of eastern North Carolina and Virginia were as high as 15–20 inches in a 24-hour period. In some areas, Floyd delivered 12–18 inches of rain, triggering regional flooding. As the storm moved northward into New England, 24-hour rainfall amounts ranged from 12 to 14 inches in Maryland, Delaware, and New Jersey. Central New Jersey, caught between a frontal system and the remnants of Hurricane Floyd, received extraordinary rainfall amounts, which triggered the worst flood event in the state in decades.

Among the unusual aspects of Hurricane Floyd, most of the significant damage was attributed to inland flooding, not coastal storm surge or high winds. There were 56 deaths attributed to Floyd in the United States—the majority blamed on inland flooding (Pasch et al. 1999).

Hurricane Floyd's impact on eastern North Carolina was unprecedented (Maiolo et al. 2001). Most of the watersheds in that part of the state experienced a 500-year flood event. One of the hardest-hit regions was the Tar-Pamlico basin and the communities of Greenville, Kinston, Tarboro, and Rocky Mount. This region of North Carolina is rural and historically black, with livelihoods based on agriculture. There is a long tradition of marginalization of these eastern North Carolina communities, which have some of the lowest income and educational levels in the state, as well as some of the highest unemployment rates. Many residents, although owning the land, live in substandard housing or in floodplains.

Much of the region housed significant hog and chicken farms that were inundated. Rotting carcasses, flooded waste lagoons, and inoperative sewage treatment plants contaminated local water supplies for months and made many of the surface water bodies extremely dangerous with waterborne pathogens. This hazard was added to the pesticides, fuels, and other contaminants already released in the floodwaters.

Two months of flooding in this region took a major toll on many of the African-American communities. Shelters were inadequate at first, and the culture of the area meant that many residents were reluctant to apply for aid from government programs, instead relying on faith-based organizations for help. Many employers gave residents some time off to recover, but often this was insufficient to complete the clean-up process, especially when families remained in the shelters because of high water. The result was that many residents were forced to make choices between jobs and taking care of their families. The elderly were hit especially hard.

Two years after Hurricane Floyd and its aftermath, many portions of eastern North Carolina had not recovered and remained just as vulnerable as they were immediately following the storm, if not more so. Many residents have resisted relocation out of floodplains and away from the family homesteads because of a strong sense of place and historic ties to the community. The town of Princeville illustrates this sense of place as well as the impact of Hurricane Floyd on these communities (see Box 4.4, p. 86). The socioeconomic inequities related to disaster assistance and need have continued, with the historically depressed regional economy remaining stagnant. The out-migration of youth means that many of these communities will age and become even more vulnerable.

State and federal disaster assistance has met with some local resistance. Pride, lack of knowledge, and an unwillingness to leave land that has been in families for generations play a key role in the refusal of aid. There has been a non-monetary loss in civic, church, and community leadership—all of which contribute to the sustenance of the rural area. It took more than a year for schools to reopen in the region, and putting the communities back together will take decades. This is a dramatic example of how patterns of social and economic inequality can affect the ability of a community to compete in the conflicted post-disaster environment. It also illustrates the extent to which a cultural group can be tied to a specific place, albeit a risky one.

CONCLUSIONS AND RECOMMENDATIONS

Conceptually we know many of the social and economic characteristics that influence human vulnerability at the individual and community level. The systematic assessment of these characteristics in any given coastal location will help communities better identify and address human vulnerability to coastal disasters. Tools such as the Framework for Assessing Vulnerability (Figure 2.1, p. 30) and the population characteristics influencing social vulnerability (presented in Table 2.2, p. 44) will help identify vulnerable populations, but additional research is needed to better understand and define the most vulnerable individuals and populations.

■ **Public and private support should promote research to better understand how individual factors known to influence human vulnerability work, and the findings used by emergency managers and disaster responders to address the needs of specific groups and places.**

Many of the forces driving coastal development, which increase the vulnerability of the human, built, and biophysical environments, are encouraged by federal, state, and local governmental policies and practices and by fractured jurisdictions in coastal environments.

■ **Federal initiatives such as the Robert T. Stafford Disaster Relief and Emergency Assistance Act, National Flood Insurance Program, beach nourishment programs, tax incentives for second homes, and infrastructure projects, as well as relevant state and local policies and practices, should be reexamined by legislative and executive bodies at all levels to reduce their role as possible stimulators of coastal growth and enhancers of vulnerability in known hazardous areas. Human and social costs should be part of the benefit–cost analysis used to determine any project's viability. Similarly, vulnerability assessments should be undertaken by all government jurisdictions as part of regular land use planning and zoning processes.**

3

HUMAN IMPACTS OF DISASTERS

WHEN EVALUATING the human impact of coastal hazards, there is a tendency to reduce losses to statistics—specifically, the number of deaths and injuries attributed directly to the initial impact. Yet, the total effects are far more extensive. This chapter discusses not only these direct impacts but also secondary and long-term physical and mental effects, health and safety, including illnesses and deaths associated with disasters, and recommends ways to reduce human suffering.

PHYSICAL HEALTH AND SAFETY

Natural hazards of significant magnitude can result in a variety of short- and long-term effects on human health and safety. Hazard events present unique health problems for those unfortunate enough to be in the direct path of high winds, heavy rain, flooding, or seismic activity. The health consequences of disasters occurring in coastal communities result primarily from changes—either natural or imposed by humans—in water quality, the land–water interface, and the built environment.

The public health consequences of natural hazards have been documented extensively for numerous major disaster events (Noji 1997). These reports focus largely on "disaster-caused" fatalities, injuries, illnesses, or other adverse health conditions resulting from the direct force of a hazard, or from events that would not have occurred in its absence (Council of State and Territorial Epidemiologists 1998). Fewer reports have addressed indirect impacts, such as those resulting from a preexisting condition exacerbated by deteriorating, interrupted public health and medical services or the disruption of normal public health or medical programs. People with preexisting illnesses, such as heart conditions or respiratory problems, tend to be at higher risk for illness, injury, or death during the initial impact or aftermath.

Additional possible impacts sometimes are reported without sufficient information to determine clearly if the effects were related, directly or indirectly, to the hazard event. With these differing definitions in mind, the next section reviews the direct and indirect impacts of hazards on the physical health of people living in coastal communities.

DEATHS AND INJURIES FROM IMPACT

Despite technological advancements, people continue to die during the pre-impact, impact, and post-impact phases of disasters, but death rates and causes have changed. Storms pose the most danger. Of the 860 fatalities reported for the 125 presidentially declared disasters from 1994 to 1998, 92 percent were attributed to climate-related disasters. Of these, 62 percent occurred in wind-related storms, 36 percent in flood-related storms, and 2 percent in severe winter storms (Jacobson et al. 2000). An estimated 50 to 100 people die annually from hurricane-related events (National Weather Service 1993).

Although property damages rose rapidly during the twentieth century, deaths from hurricanes decreased dramatically (Hebert et al. 1996). Before modern developments in forecasting and warning technologies, drowning accounted for over 90 percent of deaths (Alexander 1993, Organization of American States 1990). As the death rate has dropped, drowning continues to be the major cause of storm-related deaths (Figure 3.1).

Eight of the 15 deaths that occurred during Hurricane Hugo in South Carolina and Puerto Rico in 1989 were from drowning (Philen et al. 1992), as were 36 of the 52 fatalities associated with Hurricane Floyd. As shown in Table 3.1, two-thirds of the Hurricane Floyd drownings occurred in motor vehicles trapped in floodwater. Seven additional drowning deaths, including those of five rescue workers, occurred during transport by boat when passengers were not wearing flotation devices (Centers for Disease Control and Prevention 2000). While most of the casualties from tropical cyclones in the U.S. since 1970 were due to freshwater floods, storm surge remains the greatest risk for a large number of deaths (E. Rappaport, personal communication, 2002).

Leading Causes of Tropical Cyclone Deaths in the U.S 1970-1999

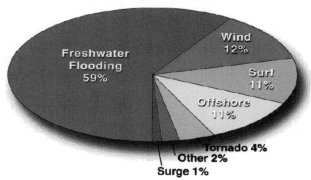

Figure 3.1 Flooding has been the leading cause of U.S. storm deaths in recent years. *Source*: Edward Rappaport, chief, Technical Support Branch, Tropical Prediction Center, Florida International University, 2002.

Although better forecasting has resulted in more people evacuating out of harm's way in advance of storms, many still are caught by rising floodwaters. Less attention tends to be paid to inland flooding, when people are caught in low-lying areas or attempt late evacuations using unsafe routes, often driving through dangerous high water. Recent evacuation

Table 3.1 Deaths Related to Hurricane Floyd in North Carolina (by cause of death)

Cause of Death	Number	Percent of Total
Drowning	36	69
In motor vehicle	24	
In boat	7	
As pedestrian	4	
In house	1	
Motor vehicle crash (excluding drowning)	7	13
Myocardial infarction	4	8
Fire (burns and trauma from escape attempts)	2	4
Hypothermia	1	2
Electrocution	1	2
Fall	1	2

Source: Centers for Disease Control and Prevention, 2000.

experiences, such as those reported for Hurricane Floyd (in which thousands of cars were gridlocked on highways for hours), are causes for major concern among emergency managers because thousands could die if caught in such situations when a storm comes ashore.

Other hazard-related deaths are caused by structural collapses of residences, especially mobile homes, and by trees falling on or near residences, places of employment, or occupied motor vehicles. In earthquakes, deaths occur when people are crushed by building materials, hit by projectiles from unsecured objects, fall, suffer burns, use gas generators improperly, or sustain trauma during escape attempts (Centers for Disease Control and Prevention 2000, Noji 1997, Philen et al. 1992). In some instances, fatalities and injuries result from a secondary event, such as a tornado spawned by a hurricane (Centers for Disease Control and Prevention 1993).

DEATHS AND INJURIES FROM CLEANUP
AND RECONSTRUCTION

Beyond those caused by direct impact, deaths related to a hazard event continue to occur for some period afterwards, as people work to put their lives and communities in order. Fatalities and injuries among workers during cleanup and reconstruction result largely from electrocution caused by the improper use of generators, lacerations from chain saws, trauma sustained because of structurally unsafe dwellings or weakened trees, and asphyxiation during entrapment under uprooted trees (Philen et al. 1992, Noji 1997). Deaths from carbon monoxide poisoning have been attributed to the improper use of generators in households without power (Centers for Disease Control and Prevention 2000). Heart attacks—probably from exertion—during structural repairs and while clearing debris account for additional deaths (Centers for Disease Control and Prevention 1996). Injuries frequently result from the use of heavy equipment.

Of the more than 2,000 patients with nonfatal hurricane-related injuries or illnesses seen in South Carolina in a two-week period immediately after Hurricane Hugo, about 88 percent were treated for their injuries, nearly one-third of which were related to the use of chain saws (Brewer et al. 1994). One study of a hospital emergency department reported hydrocarbon or bleach poisoning among children during the clean-up phase (Quinn et al. 1994). After hurricanes Hugo, Opal, and Floyd, the proportion of medical problems at emergency rooms associated with insect bites increased substantially (Centers for Disease Control and Prevention 1996, Brewer et al. 1994). Sprains, contusions, and fractures constituted the remaining spectrum of minor injuries. Hypothermia and dog bites also occurred in excess of the usual incidence (Centers for Disease Control and Prevention 2000).

ILLNESSES ASSOCIATED WITH DEBRIS AND POLLUTION

Additional health problems result from detrimental environmental conditions. Respiratory illnesses have been documented in connection with numerous hazard events and may be exacerbated by exposure to extreme temperatures and conditions during displacement and cleanup (Figure 3.2). Dust from damaged buildings can cause eye and respiratory tract irritations. Mildew, mold, ash from burning debris, and construction dust can aggravate asthmatic conditions and other breathing-related problems. Aside from physically affecting air passages and lungs, dust may be contaminated with asbestos and other toxic materials, posing an additional environmental hazard to rescue and clean-up personnel.

Figure 3.2 Wearing protective clothing, volunteer cleanup crews move from house to house in Tarboro, North Carolina. *Source*: Dave Saville/FEMA News Photo.

Respiratory illnesses increased in south Dade County, Florida, during the first five weeks after Hurricane Andrew (Lee et al. 1993). Similarly, outbreaks of self-limiting respiratory and gastrointestinal illnesses occurred in shelters in North Carolina after Hurricane Floyd (Centers for Disease Control and Prevention 2000). The number of asthma cases, in particular, increased substantially.

The risk of waterborne disease is high (Mallin et al. 2000). Flooding increases the potential for environmental contamination when inundated toxic waste sites release harmful chemicals stored at ground level (Showalter and Myers 1994). Floodwaters may flush agricultural chemicals and pesticides into residential areas and rivers, resulting in elevated levels of chlorinated and organophosphate pesticides in study adolescents (Balluz et al. 2001). Illnesses occur when water treatment and sewage disposal systems are disrupted, thereby affecting water quality and food safety. In these situations, waterborne diseases may be transmitted, with outbreaks of such diseases expected in areas where they are endemic (Noji 1997).

In 1996 in southeastern North Carolina, the risk for human illness from severe water-quality problems was heightened when post-hurricane flooding caused massive amounts of swamp water to be diverted into river channels, power failures at sewage treatment and pump stations diverted raw sewage into rivers, and breaching of several swine waste lagoons diverted large quantities of concentrated organic waste into river systems (Mallin et al. 1999). Thousands of aboveground fuel tanks broke away in the flooding after Hurricane Floyd (Federal Emergency Management Agency 2001).

Although studies are few, long-term health effects have been observed after flooding. A cluster of deaths attributed to leukemia and lymphoma and a cluster of abnormal reproductive outcomes were reported related to a flood event in a river valley in western New York in 1972 (Janerich et al. 1981). Illnesses and defects were attributed to high levels of natural background radiation in surface rock deposits, radiation from a nearby nuclear processing plant, and radiation suspected to have originated from a well.

In summary, although the death and injury toll from coastal hazards has been reduced dramatically in spite of increased coastal urbanization, considerable cause for concern remains. The potential for loss of human life would be enormous if, for example, a Category 5 hurricane hit an urbanized coastal area directly. If major mitigation efforts are not undertaken beforehand, the death toll is likely to be higher than anything experienced in modern history. The good news is that many, if not most, of the deaths and injuries that occur in the aftermath of a hazard event can be avoided with proper warning, education, and response. Some specific ideas for reducing deaths and injuries are provided at the end of this chapter (p. 76–77). Some, such as better evacuation procedures, require major public initiatives and expenditures, whereas others require education to change risky behavior, such as driving through high floodwaters or using chain saws improperly.

MENTAL HEALTH

Although most people exhibit no lasting mental or emotional effects after experiencing a disaster event, some do. For every person physically injured, there may be anywhere from four to 20 psychological victims, and these can be more difficult to identify. Most people show some signs of stress as normal responses to a very abnormal event, but these usually resolve naturally over time (American Psychiatric Association 2000).

PHASES OF EMOTIONAL REACTIONS

People tend to display a range of emotional reactions to a disaster event that can be divided loosely into four phases, as summarized by Weaver (1995):

Heroic Phase: Beginning immediately after the event, people tend to work together to do whatever is necessary, even risking personal danger to assist in the rescue of strangers or to salvage property. Relief workers and victims can experience adrenaline rushes that enable them to perform unusual feats of strength or endurance, often working long hours without adequate rest or nutrition.

Honeymoon Phase: During this phase, which may last for several weeks, there is an outpouring of relief efforts and supplies, and victims are openly grateful. They may be highly optimistic about their ability to recover quickly, tending to underestimate the impact of their losses. Community spirit and altruism is common, with neighbors pitching in to salvage possessions and to share resources.

Disillusionment Phase: Within a few weeks, reality sinks in, as people grow impatient with long lines, waiting periods, and bureaucracies.

Competition for scarce resources replaces the cooperative spirit of the early aftermath. Some feel betrayed as assistance falls short of expectations. Others are victimized a second time by unscrupulous contractors, price gouging, high interest rates, changes in zoning regulations, bankrupt insurance companies, and a shortage of building materials or qualified repair and construction services. Anger, frustration, and helplessness may turn into despair, depression, and hopelessness that can persist for years.

Reconstruction Phase: This period usually begins several months after the event and becomes the "new normal" state. Normal functioning begins to be reestablished, and life settles into new patterns.

Although homes and public buildings may be rebuilt, businesses reopened, and roads and bridges repaired, the community is never quite the same. Some structures are not rebuilt, some families never return, and some businesses remain closed. Many people forever mark time differently, describing events as either before or after the disaster.

Signs of Stress

Signs of post-disaster stress are typically short-lived, but severe reactions may last from 18 to 36 months (Solomon and Green 1992), and up to six years if the disaster is due to human-induced factors (Healey 2001). The effects of post-disaster stress can show up in a variety of ways, which the American Psychiatric Association (2000) has divided into four general categories:

Emotional Reactions: Victims may experience depression, lingering fear and anxiety, shock, and numbness, often characterized by blank stares. Some grieve, whereas others feel guilt and shame, either at their lack of adequate preparation or at having lost so much less than others have. They may be embarrassed at accepting "charity." They may feel anger, resentment, or restlessness. Sounds, sights, or smells can trigger sudden and unwelcome memories, along with strong emotional reactions (see Box 3.1).

Behavioral Problems: Mood swings, suspicion, irritability, and apathy can occur. Some victims turn to the numbing effects of alcohol or other drugs (Solomon and Green 1992). Reactions such as post-traumatic stress disorder and depression have been documented. Less is known about suicide; although the authors of an often-cited suicide study (Krug

---

Box 3.1 Memories and Fears

A year after the Venezuelan mudslides in 1999, survivors became fearful of being separated from their families every time rain clouds appeared. The sound of rain and the smell of mud instantly brought back the frightening memories (Kriner 2000). Residents of South Florida reported five years after 1992's Hurricane Andrew that they felt they would never lose the fear and apprehension they experienced every time a storm appeared. One couple noted that even the family dog whimpered and cried when a storm approached (Neal 1997).

---

et al. 1998) later retracted some U.S. results, they stand by their analysis of data from 70 countries affected by two disasters that documented an increased suicide rate (Bowman 1999). Talk of suicide, expressions of excessive guilt or anxiety, and substance abuse are all warning signals requiring immediate professional attention. There is growing evidence that domestic violence increases after a major disaster, sometimes escalating in relationships in which it already existed (Wilson et al. 1998, Enarson and Morrow 1997).

Cognitive Effects: Some victims have difficulty making realistic recovery plans or even participating in clean-up efforts because of confusion, disorientation, and indecisiveness. Some suffer memory loss or have short attention spans (Solomon and Green 1992). Relief workers may have to repeat assistance application instructions several times. Anxiety can reduce productivity at work or school (Weaver 1995).

Physical Symptoms: Tension, fatigue, edginess, sleep difficulties, aches and pains, rapid heart rate, nausea, change in appetite, and loss of libido all have been linked to trauma from disasters. Some people experience nightmares in which they relive the experience (Weaver 1995). Heightened rates of abdominal problems, amnesia, paralysis, fainting, and double vision have been reported in hurricane victims (Escobar et al. 1992). Evaluations one year after Hurricane Andrew revealed that many victims had sleep disturbances. Those with prior sleeping problems were more likely to develop post-disaster stress problems (Mellman et al. 1995). Most symptoms are short-lived, but some stress-related problems, such as increased respiratory, cardiac, and digestive symptoms, have been documented up to five years after a disaster (Krug et al. 1998).

BLENDING OF PHYSICAL AND EMOTIONAL PROBLEMS

The line between physical and mental health problems is not always clear. Stress and disrupted eating and sleeping patterns can exacerbate symptoms associated with chronic health problems, such as diabetes, asthma, cardiac problems, ulcers, and seizure disorders (Weaver 1995). South Florida residents directly exposed to the fury of Hurricane Andrew reported higher rates of relapse and recurrence of chronic diseases than did residents of areas that experienced less direct impact (Lutgendorf et al. 1995). Level of emotional stress was the single strongest predictor of the probability and severity of exacerbation of pre-disaster health problems and the extent to which normal functioning was worsened. Those who benefited from optimism and good social supports had significantly lower rates of illness after the hurricane.

Many factors in the post-disaster environment can make it extremely difficult for people to cope and to carry out routine recovery tasks. Community disruption, changes in routine, loss of social supports, rumors, misinformation, and further bad weather can be additional stressors. It can take weeks, months, or even years to overcome completely the effects of disaster trauma, and, even then, there can be a recurrence of symptoms during stressful times such as divorce, retirement, or loss of a loved one (American Psychiatric Association 2000).

FACTORS ASSOCIATED WITH PSYCHOLOGICAL EFFECTS

Some factors associated with psychological effects have to do with the characteristics of a hazard event, and others with the personal circumstances of those affected (Healey 2001, American Psychiatric Association 2000, Rekenthaler 1999, Krug et al. 1998).

Nature of Hazard Event

Certain types of disaster experiences tend to be especially stressful. Hazard events with the following characteristics have been associated with high emotional impact:

- Severe impact
- Long duration

- Lack of warning
- Occurrence of injuries and deaths
- Darkness, power outages
- Possibility of recurrence
- Widespread community destruction
- Human-induced as opposed to natural cause

Some of these characteristics are self-explanatory. People who endure a severe and long-lasting hazard that results in many deaths clearly are at high risk for emotional problems. Sudden events, especially if there is a chance they will occur again—such as earthquakes and aftershocks—are more traumatic than events such as hurricanes, for which there is more time to prepare.

Dark nights associated with long periods of power outages can be frightening. Although the psychological consequences of personal property loss tend to be relatively short-term, lasting less than one year for most people, exposure to widespread community destruction has been found to have a longer-term impact (up to two years), regardless of individual loss (Solomon and Green 1992). Living in a devastated neighborhood lacking familiar sights, services, and people can be depressing and stressful, even when a person's own home has escaped damage. If their own and their neighbors' homes have been destroyed or badly damaged, people can have an especially difficult time coping, particularly during long recovery periods.

Human-induced disasters, such as terrorist attacks, gas leaks, or other technological events, tend to affect people more than do natural ones. The psychological effects are likely to be greater and more long lasting. As described by Erikson (1994) in *A New Species of Trouble*, disasters caused by human action are more likely to be preventable and thus more difficult to accept when they occur.

Personal Factors

Certain attributes, backgrounds, and life experience factors leave some people more vulnerable than others to mental health effects:

- History of previous mental health problem
- Recent or disaster-caused death of a loved one

- Direct exposure to the more horrific aspects of a disaster, including death and mass devastation
- Living alone or lacking adequate support systems
- Renting rather than owning a home
- Lack of resources (e.g., money, education, physical health) to respond to damage and hardships
- Lack of personal preparedness, resulting in self-blame for the hardships endured by self and loved ones

Several of these factors require some explanation. Homeowners tend to have insurance and other resources to help overcome losses, and they tend to have more control over repair or relocation decisions than do renters. More assistance programs are available to help homeowners. Renters lack control over the circumstances of their housing, including whether hazard mitigation actions are taken. Renters make up the majority of the dislocated found in tent cities and temporary housing, living under very stressful conditions after major disasters. In tight housing markets in areas with heavy destruction, landlords often raise rents beyond the reach of former tenants.

Activities such as assembling emergency supplies, making evacuation plans, and taking mitigation actions to safeguard homes and families provide some sense of control over the situation and can help insulate a person from emotional trauma (Healey 2001). As an example, those living in high-risk coastal areas can take a number of precautions against hurricanes, including protecting windows. Yet, according to a recent survey, 62 percent of Florida's homeowners have no window coverage or shutter system (Peacock et al. 2001). Another study revealed that only 41 percent of high-risk hurricane residents reported having an evacuation plan (Healy 2001).

POPULATIONS AT RISK FOR
HEALTH-RELATED PROBLEMS

Human vulnerability in general tends to be associated with limited resources or options. As discussed in Chapter 2, certain coastal residents tend to be more vulnerable to the effects of hazards and thus at higher risk for death, injury, and mental health problems. Although a great deal of variability exists within groups, evidence from past events confirms that several categories of coastal residents tend to be at higher risk for human impacts.

THE ELDERLY AND THE DISABLED

Vulnerability among the elderly varies significantly with age, health, family status, and economic resources, but older residents as a group are more likely to lack the physical and economic resources necessary for effective response and recovery and are more likely to suffer health-related consequences (Figure 3.3) (Tobin and Ollenburger 1993, Russell and Cutrona 1991, Huerta and Horton 1978). Older residents tend to be reluctant to evacuate to escape hurricanes (Gladwin and Peacock 2000), creating a higher potential for injury and loss of life. Changes in daily routines and landscapes following an event can be especially disorienting. The loss of sentimental items, such as photos, the family *Bible*, or antiques, may be felt acutely as a loss of precious ties to their past (Weaver 1995).

Long-term adult living facilities and hospitals pose serious challenges during hazard events. When frail elderly are forced to evacuate or relocate, the trauma can be life threatening. There is no official record of premature deaths due to a disaster, but some evidence suggests that they do occur. There was a rise in the death rate in the months following Hurricane Andrew, perhaps attributable to the stress of daily living in a

Figure 3.3 Older adults can find it particularly difficult to cope with a hazard event. *Source:* FEMA News Photo.

destroyed community (Morrow 1997). Anecdotal accounts and logic lead to the conclusion that many of these were likely premature deaths of frail elderly residents.

CHILDREN

The vulnerability of children is self-evident, and many studies have examined the psychological effects of disaster events on them (Shannon et al. 1994, Jones et al. 1993, Green et al. 1991). Major hazard-related events often cause behavioral changes in children, including sleep disturbances (Weaver 1995). Many react with fear and are anxious about a recurrence. Adolescents are prone to bouts of depression and anxiety, whereas younger children demonstrate regressive behaviors, such as thumb sucking and bedwetting, associated with earlier developmental stages. Children may be less resilient than many assume, and they may experience confusion and loss at a time when their parents are absorbed in the clean-up process and obtaining recovery assistance.

Children who have no opportunity to talk out their feelings about an event can develop feelings of guilt, shame, or being unloved (Center for Mental Health Services 2000). Studies show that parents often fail to recognize signs of distress, particularly anxiety, in their children (Solomon and Green 1992). Children tend to take cues from the reactions of parents and other authority figures; thus, parental distress can largely determine a child's reactions (Solomon and Green 1992).

Children may avoid school; a delayed return can lead to the development of phobias and other problems. When buildings are damaged or used as shelters, schools may be closed and students bused to unfamiliar buildings to attend class with unfamiliar peers, further adding to the stress (Weaver 1995). Some parents become overprotective and fearful of being separated from their children, so they may be reluctant to allow them to return to school (Kriner 2000). Parents absorbed in their own trauma and recovery activities may have little energy left for their children's emotional needs. Single parents in particular may have little time to deal with the emotional issues their children face. Several studies indicate there are gender differences, with young girls appearing to be more adversely affected emotionally (Center for Mental Health Services 2000, Solomon and Green 1992, Burke et al. 1986).

Typical reactions of children to disasters are listed in Table 3.2. The onset and duration of these reactions vary with each child, but most would be considered normal as long as they do not persist for more than two to three months. Many factors influence the extent to which a child will be affected, including proximity to the danger, severity of the event, type of personal losses, and reactions of adult role models. It should also be mentioned that some positive experiences and reactions could also occur. Children can also be empowered when helping with cleanup and recovery work.

WOMEN

As will be discussed in more detail in the next chapter, there is a growing body of literature related to women and disasters (Morrow and Phillips 1999, Enarson and Morrow 1998, Fothergill 1996, Morrow and Enarson 1996). Continuing social role expectations result in women bearing most of the responsibility for domestic and caregiving tasks, and these become more difficult when disaster strikes. Women tend to suffer more serious emotional distress than do men (Van Willigen 2001), partially because the physical and emotional effects of housing losses have greater implications for women (Enarson 1999). Dislocated women may be more strongly affected by the disruption in friendships and kinship networks. See Figure 3.4.

Following Hurricane Floyd, women in counties with moderate to severe flooding reported lower levels of social support and purpose to their lives than did women living elsewhere. Studies of Gulf Coast residents after Hurricane George showed a significant deterioration in social support during the post-impact period (Adola 1999). The loss of support systems can be a factor in the higher rates of depression among women (Van Willigen 2001).

In contrast, there is evidence that some men feel stronger and perceive a greater sense of purpose in their lives following a disaster, especially if they are active in the home repair and recovery process (Van Willigen 2001). This coincides with research findings that white males, in particular, tend to be less concerned about hazard risks in general, maybe "because they are more involved in creating, managing, controlling and benefiting from technology and other activities that are hazardous" (Slovic 2000, p. xxxiv). In other words, they are more likely than women to feel they have power and can control situations. On the other hand, men who

Table 3.2   Typical Reactions of Children to Disasters

Age of Child	Reaction
Preschool	Crying Confusion Clinging Eating problems Immobility Sadness Irritability Speech problems Baby talk Sensitivity to loud noise Nightmares/night terrors Fear of animals, darkness Fear of rain or thunder Loss of bowel/bladder control Afraid to sleep alone or without lights Fear of being left alone Fear of strangers Need help with feeding Need help to dress
6–11 years old	Irrational fears Headache Nausea Visual problems Hearing problems Disobedience Distractibility Fighting Trouble concentrating Peer problems Social withdrawal School problems Inability to enjoy previous fun activities
12 –17 years old	Headaches Other physical complaints Confusion Depression Suicidal ideation Social isolation Poor performance Aggressive behavior Withdrawal Sleep disturbances School problems Antisocial behavior (stealing, vandalism)

Source: Weaver 1995 (from the work of Lystad 1985 and Farberow and Gordon 1981).

Figure 3.4 The physical and emotional effects of housing loss can be especially difficult for women. *Source*: Andrea Booher/FEMA News Photo.

feel stressed often find it more difficult to ask for and accept help, especially mental health counseling.

MINORITIES AND THE POOR

Disasters are not equal-opportunity events. Effects are likely to be greater than average for minorities and the poor. Storm mortality rates are typically relatively high among the poor, who are more likely to live in substandard housing located in floodplains and other vulnerable locations (Blaikie et al. 1994). Although the data are sometimes contradictory, mortality rates also tend to be relatively high among minorities (Bolin and Bolton 1986, Bates et al. 1963). Their homes tend to be less well-built and maintained, devoid of disaster mitigation initiatives, and thus less safe. Therefore, it is reasonable to assume that these homes are more likely to sustain damage and become unsafe.

After a major event, minorities and/or poor survivors are more likely to live in temporary and or damaged housing, often under difficult conditions for long periods, with high potential for depression and emotional problems, violence and relationship problems, and health problems such as respiratory illnesses (Morrow 1997, Phillips 1993). African-Americans, the poor, and the disabled remained in shelters longer than other residents did after hurricanes Bertha, Bonnie, and Floyd (Hazards

Workshop Summary #16 2000). Uninsured losses, unemployment, loss of public transportation, and other lost services can have especially devastating health effects on those lacking the resources to get through a crisis in a timely manner.

The disaster resiliency of a community revolves around the ability of all residents to afford secure housing. In poorer communities, this might necessitate the availability of low-interest mortgage loans; disaster-resilient, government-subsidized housing; and other housing and hazard mitigation incentives. Although the NFIP provides moderately priced flood insurance, insurance against earthquakes, wind, and other hazards is not as readily available. When minority homeowners are insured, the agencies are likely to be marginal or unstable (Peacock and Girard 2000). Low-income elderly homeowners often drop their insurance to pay for more pressing needs, such as food and medicine.

There is a growing theoretical approach to disaster mitigation that focuses on the root causes of vulnerability within a society, such as poverty, exploitation, and marginalization (Anderson 2000). For a community to be truly disaster-resilient, all citizens need access to affordable means with which to mitigate and respond. It seems inconsistent in a democratic society for a safe home environment to be available only to those who can afford it (Boyce 2000). As stated by Phillips (2002, p. 9), "To reduce loss of life and injuries and to protect property, we must reduce vulnerability based on ethnicity, culture, national origin, disability, age, gender, or social class. If we want to reduce vulnerability, we must work for justice."

An important first step is to understand how social and economic conditions place certain categories of residents at a disadvantage, and then to determine where these groups tend to be clustered in a given local community, how their circumstances can be improved, and how they can best be mobilized on their own behalf. This requires not only collecting census and other data, but also seeking out and engaging neighborhoods and groups to identify local vulnerabilities collaboratively. The next step is to collaborate with these local groups to help them use their capacities to reduce risks and improve their ability to respond to coastal disasters.

EVACUATION BEHAVIOR

Hurricane Floyd led to massive evacuations along the entire southeastern coast of the United States. Whitehead et al. (2001), in *Facing Our Future:*

Hurricane Floyd and Recovery in the Coastal Plain describe the dynamics of disaster evacuation behavior. The paper states "understanding hurricane evacuation behavior and the ability to make informed predictions based on that behavior is an important tool for emergency managers. The manager issues evacuation orders, reverses highway lanes, closes bridges, and makes other decisions that directly concern evacuees." Information is essential for emergency planners to understand why people behave the way they do and the economic impacts of their behavior during disasters.

For evacuees along the Atlantic Coast (Figure 3.5), Hurricane Floyd was a false alarm. Evacuation costs were incurred without a corresponding increase in personal safety. The research done for the Whitehead et al. (2001) paper compared evacuation behaviors from Hurricanes Bonnie, Dennis, and Floyd. They found that evacuation decisions depend on such things such as pet ownership, receiving evacuation orders, and whether or not residents lived in a mobile home. Important factors in determining evacuation for Bonnie were the risk of flooding, gender, and levels of education, while race was an important determinate for Dennis. Unfortunately, not all residents in storm surge zones evacuate. And, some residents who are not at risk from flooding evacuate their homes, causing traffic problems and overflows at shelters and motels. Whitehead et al. (2001) recommend that pet-friendly shelters and motels be created so pet owners would feel more comfortable about leaving their homes.

Figure 3.5 The exodus continued in the few hours before Hurricane Floyd hit Wilmington, North Carolina, with most off the traffic headed west out of harms way. *Source*: Dave Gatley/FEMA News Photo.

Education about the risk of flooding would also improve the evacuation decision process.

CONCLUSIONS AND RECOMMENDATIONS

Not enough is known about the unique mechanisms that lead to specific deaths, injuries, and illnesses associated with disasters. Current information tends to be sketchy, particularly concerning the situational details associated with disasters and information about victims. To develop effective education, mitigation, and response programs, planners need a better understanding of situations that arise during disasters and health impacts on target populations.

> ■ **New methodologies and research initiatives should be developed by the Centers for Disease Prevention and Control and other related organizations to better quantify and describe health-related outcomes of coastal disasters, identifying populations most at risk for specific problems.**

There is a growing body of evidence that many—indeed most— of the deaths and injuries associated with coastal hazards do not occur at the time of direct impact. In most hurricanes, the greatest havoc is created, not by winds and coastal surges, but rather by inland flooding. Cleanup and reconstruction activities also can be very dangerous, as evidenced by the number of chain saw accidents, falls from roofs, and other accidents reported. Because of a general lack of systematic recording, the actual number of accidents is likely to be much higher than is suggested by the data.

> ■ **At all levels, from federal to local, education and outreach programs should be developed to target lesser-known dangers from cleanup and reconstruction activities such as drowning as a result of driving in hazardous areas after a storm, or not using flotation devices during flood rescues and injuries from the inappropriate use of chain saws, generators, and other equipment in the aftermath of an event.**

The multistate traffic gridlock that occurred when millions attempted to evacuate before Hurricane Floyd highlighted the dangers associated with mass evacuation. More effective ways must be found to help people realistically assess and respond to the risks, prevent unnecessary evacuation, provide safe sanctuaries closer to home, and better manage the safe evacuation of those who should leave.

■ **Evacuation issues should be part of land use decisions in coastal areas. Federal and state transportation agencies need to develop multi-state evacuation policies and plans for coastal areas. More research is needed to better understand how people make evacuation decisions. Technologies, such as computer modeling and the visualization of the effects of storm surge and flooding in specific locations, can help citizens evaluate their level of risk. Extensive education programs should be implemented to assist people in coastal areas to make wiser evacuation decisions, emphasizing the hazards of unnecessary or untimely evacuation. Alternatives, such as home shuttering and safe local shelters, should be promoted through loan programs, public shelter funding, and other government incentives.**

The importance of social support systems in combating the mental health effects of disasters has been well established. People recover more quickly when they are embedded in social networks of family, friends, and neighbors.

■ **Response agencies at all levels should pay special attention to promoting and protecting social networks when planning policies and community response programs. To the extent possible, family and neighborhood groups should be kept together when temporary sheltering or housing is assigned. Programs and facilities should be planned to promote formal and informal social interaction in the aftermath of a disaster.**

There is no substitute for mitigation and preparedness. Not only is the impact likely to be reduced, but the psychological consequences associated with injury and damage is also lessened. Even when a person's home is damaged in spite of mitigation actions, the emotional impact tends to be lessened because those efforts had been made. People do best when they have the knowledge, resources, and opportunities to take mitigation and response actions on their own behalf.

■ **Mitigation measures need to be reexamined by taking into account a broader set of impacts, including the social costs of disasters. Those initiatives shown to be cost effective should be expanded through educational and outreach programs, special incentives, and resources to assist high-risk populations.**

4

COMMUNITY AND
INSTITUTIONAL IMPACTS

IT IS OFTEN SAID that disasters tear apart the social fabric of communities. The destruction and disruption caused by a major hurricane, flood, or earthquake can virtually close down a community, including its institutions and social networks, making it difficult, if not impossible, for people to continue with the routines of daily life. Some effects are short-term, erased when roads are cleared, utilities repaired, and businesses reopened. Other effects take longer to disappear or may change a community permanently—for better or worse. This chapter examines how the major institutions that serve communities can be affected when a coastal region sustains severe impacts from a disaster.

POLITICAL INSTITUTIONS

Every major natural disaster seems to be followed by a "political disaster." Most governments, particularly at the local level, are not prepared to deal adequately with the heavy demands. In the past, municipalities rarely have had adequate disaster plans in place, and, even when prepared for immediate emergency and relief needs, most have not planned for recovery, much less for incorporating mitigation initiatives into reconstruction projects.

       Local governments take a variety of forms in the United States— city or municipality, county, district, parish—and there is considerable variation in the extent to which they are autonomous, have adequate tax bases, provide local services, and possess power within the larger structure of state politics. This variation often leads to uneven recovery patterns within the same general region. People tend to associate Hurricane Andrew with Homestead, Florida, yet most of the damage occurred outside Homestead's city limits in unincorporated Dade County, areas that received far less attention during relief and recovery. This was in large part due to the city's relations with other governmental entities. Political savvy played a role as well. Within days of the storm, the city of Homestead employed a public relations firm to get the word out about conditions there. The only other incorporated municipality in the heavily affected area was Florida City, a largely African-American community lacking similar power and resources. Its experiences mirrored those of Santa Cruz and Watsonville, California, after the Loma Prieta earthquake, when media attention was focused on San Francisco (Sibley 1995). Interestingly, Florida City received fewer FEMA grant funds per capita than did Homestead, even though its needs were equal or greater (Dash et al. 1997). However, the long-term recovery process has been difficult for the city of Homestead, largely because of the void created by management losses and leadership changes in the aftermath. In contrast, Florida City has a strong mayor who has been in continuous service and has been successful in attracting new economic interests, again pointing to the important role of local government at all stages of disaster response.

States vary in political power as well as the extent to which emergency response and disaster management responsibilities are emphasized and funded. As might be expected, high-risk coastal states, such as California, Florida, and North Carolina, tend to place a higher priority on emergency management than do other states, and they also tend to be better organized to respond and get federal resources moving into their states when needed. Leadership on key congressional committees can be an important advantage in getting federal disaster declarations and appropriations.

Regardless of how well the system is organized, the inevitable chaos of the immediate aftermath, the competitive nature of the recovery process as it is played out in the United States, and the painfully slow pace of the process—even under the best of circumstances—result in a great deal of human suffering. The many contingencies and different sets of circumstances result in winners and losers; invariably, many people will be unhappy with both the pace and results. These people tend to blame someone, and those held responsible, in turn, tend to blame someone else. The political implications are many.

Public officials usually withstand the worst of the finger pointing. In his discussion of disaster politics, Olson (2000) offers six disaster excuses often used by public officials to deny personal responsibility: (1) blaming the event, (2) blaming "the previous guy," (3) blaming the context, (4) blaming "us all," (5) blaming "them" up/down there, and (6) the plea of ignorance. As examples, Downton and Pielke (2001) note that a former FEMA director suggested that climatologic changes and freak weather events play a principal role in the increased frequency of presidentially declared disasters. In blaming the event, there is a tendency to overplay the occurrence—in essence, calling any hurricane that causes major damage the "big one," as was the case with Hurricane Andrew, even though it was far from the event of an emergency manager's worst nightmares in terms of size, strength, and rainfall. One national study explains the rising cost of natural hazards as "part of an inevitable consequence of population growth and rising wealth" (Natural Hazards Caucus Work Group 2001), essentially blaming these hazards on everyone, or at least those who live along the coasts who have enjoyed an increase in living standard. Federal authorities point to the need for stronger state building codes, and states in turn point out that codes and code enforcement are primarily the responsibility of local governments.

It is not unusual, and in fact is quite typical, for this "blame game" to result in political change. Nearly every disaster has an example of a public "scapegoat." The defeat of the reelection bid of the governor of the U.S. Virgin Islands was largely attributed to perceptions of leadership failure after Hurricane Hugo in 1989. Santa Cruz has had four city managers since the Loma Prieta earthquake, a turnover largely attributed to unhappiness with the recovery process.

The distribution of resources coming into a stricken community also takes on a political dimension. Incumbents may not be able to resist the temptation to use this opportunity to bestow political "gifts" on the favored. There is a tendency for presidents to award funds to states based on factors other than need (Downton and Pielke 2001, Sylves 1996). According to Platt (1999), the only federal program that is needs based is the individual assistance program administered by FEMA. Yet, even the distribution of those funds can take on a political dimension, at least in terms of timing. Just days after Hurricane Andrew, FEMA field operatives were instructed to "fast track" as many loan and grant applications as possible, even though there were very few stores or banks open for business within 20 miles. Some attributed this haste to the presidential election going into its final days (Polny 1993). Even federal mitigation initiatives, such as Project Impact, became highly politicized (Box 4.1).

Box 4.1 Project Impact Critique

Through the former Project Impact program, FEMA provided pre-disaster mitigation funding to communities to support a range of activities, including public–private partnership formation, community planning, and implementation of innovative and long-term mitigation solutions. Piloted in November 1997, the project became the centerpiece of FEMA under the Clinton Administration, effectively supplanting many other mitigation initiatives and funding sources (Platt 1999). Project Impact communities were found in each of the 50 states as well as the Virgin Islands and Puerto Rico.

In theory, the idea of bringing together the full range of stakeholders—community groups, all levels of government, the private sector—appeared to be a recipe for success in community-based mitigation planning (Heinz Center 2000b). In practice, the initiative took on a distinctly political quality. From the revival-like annual summits to logo placements on baseball caps and racecars, Project Impact was intensely concerned with launching a corporate-style marketing campaign. State officials, other federal agencies, and neighboring communities were often left out. With few exceptions, FEMA selected the initial Project Impact communities with little input from the state offices of emergency management. In the pilot community of Deerfield Beach, Florida, FEMA funded the retrofit of a high school as a shelter in spite of the fact that the project was not part of countywide local mitigation strategy or on the state's shelter retrofit schedule.

Although Project Impact did much to promote mitigation and increased mitigation awareness in a host of communities, some say the implementation left out the interests of a range of stakeholders and sacrificed good planning.

With the passage of the Disaster Mitigation Act of 2000, Project Impact has ended, being replaced by the Pre-Disaster Mitigation funding to the States. FEMA is now placing more emphasis on community-based plans. Learning from the lessons of Project Impact, the establishment of planning criteria and the process for developing these plans must include a range of appropriate stakeholders, including states and local governments, to avoid ending up with a one-size-fits-all plan that does little to meet state and local needs.

The federal funds distributed following a presidentially declared disaster serve to boost a local economy, at least temporarily. Under the Stafford Disaster Relief and Emergency Assistance Act of 1993, the federal government provides funds to cover at least 75 percent of the costs of rehabilitating public facilities. For catastrophic events, such as Hurricane

Andrew and the 1993 Mississippi floods, the federal government covers the entire cost of public facility repairs; 90 percent of such costs were covered after the Northridge earthquake, with the remainder financed by the state of California.

It is, therefore, not surprising that most municipalities have shown little interest in investing in loss reduction measures for their facilities; city officials have reason to assume that future damage will be covered by federal or state assistance. Local governments have been slow to adopt mitigation measures or to purchase insurance against losses to their buildings (Burby 1992). A study by French and Rudholm (1990) of damage to public property in the 1987 Whittier Narrows (California) earthquake revealed that few public buildings were protected by earthquake insurance, even though it was readily available from the private sector.

With respect to the private sector, the federal government offers low-interest (4–8 percent) loans to qualified uninsured and underinsured disaster victims through a Small Business Administration (SBA) disaster loan program. These programs can be costly to taxpayers if many loans are provided at below-market rates. From 1953 through 2001, the SBA loaned more than $28 billion to disaster victims (Small Business Administration 2001).

Political changes after a major disaster are not always negative. Although the immediate effects can be disconcerting, especially to those in power, the net result can benefit the community as a whole. It is not unusual for grassroots groups, including minority voices, to become

Figure 4.1 A patriotic couple embrace as they survey the damage done to their home by Hurricane Andrew. *Source*: FEMA News Photo.

engaged in the decisions related to recovery. When disasters reveal patterns of neglect, city leaders may be forced to recognize minority citizens and poor neighborhoods in new ways. We Will Rebuild, the umbrella group of community leaders that coordinated the distribution of millions of private and public funds in South Florida after Hurricane Andrew, was confronted by new coalitions of organizations representing women, minorities, and religious groups demanding a role in funding decisions (Box 4.2). Increased activism by minority groups was reflected in the outcomes of subsequent municipal and county elections (Morrow and Peacock 2000).

Smaller communities often get lost in the bureaucratic morass associated with post-disaster resources. Unincorporated areas may not receive the same level of advocacy as areas with municipal representation in the political arena. Similarly, rural areas may not receive their due attention. Delia (2001) attributes the absence of appropriate attention to the floods of 1999 in eastern North Carolina to the region's lack of political

---

Box 4.2 Women Will Rebuild

After Hurricane Andrew, at the personal request of then-President George Bush, local business leaders in Miami formed an organization to oversee the collection and allocation of donations (and later public funds). In all, We Will Rebuild eventually distributed more than $27 million in private funds and directed billions of public dollars to targeted programs. Not surprisingly, rebuilding the economic infrastructure was the top priority of this group, which believed that the recovery of the rest of the community would follow naturally. To the families housed in tent cities, doubled up in partially destroyed houses, occupying condemned apartment buildings, and living in other dismal circumstances, the pace of recovery was painfully slow. Many felt there was an excessive focus on business and long-term economic recovery at a time when thousands still were suffering from a lack of necessities and community services

In counterpoint, Women Will Rebuild emerged as a coalition of existing women's groups calling for more attention to the crisis needs of women and their families. Their long struggle for legitimacy and action fell short of many of the group's goals, but it drew public attention to immediate health and social service needs and, in the end, achieved some additional financial resources for women and children in south Dade County—and a greater voice for women in disaster recovery (Enarson and Morrow 1998).

muscle. The flooded land mass was larger than Rhode Island, Connecticut, and Massachusetts combined, but, in his opinion, these more urban and affluent regions would have received a far greater federal response.

Disasters can be focusing events for reordering public policy agendas (Birkland 1997). They can illustrate dramatically the effects of poor land use, environmental degradation, inadequate building codes, and other planning failures, leading to renewed concern for the environment, land use planning, and construction standards. In this way, disasters can provide unique opportunities for the development of mitigation initiatives that lead to safer communities. The escalation of economic costs in recent disasters has created a strong impetus for prevention. At the federal level, major policy changes at FEMA have led to new funding opportunities for state and local mitigation projects. Florida and South Carolina have newly mandated, statewide building codes inspired by the numerous hurricanes that have come ashore in recent years, particularly Andrew and Hugo (Mittler 1998). At the local level, Oakland, California, is recognized as an excellent example of a city emerging from its Loma Prieta experience with major policy and institutional changes that have increased its resilience to future earthquakes (Olson et al. 1998 and 1999).

Even mitigation initiatives are not without their political downside, often causing a great deal of public controversy. Major confrontations can occur when communities starting to rebuild are limited by new land development controls or zoning regulations (Box 4.3).

Olson and Olson (1993) document the local struggle to address redevelopment and mitigation in the post-disaster environment of Oroville, California, after a 1975 earthquake. In a drawn-out process of political give-and-take involving a range of stakeholders, the will to support post-disaster seismic retrofitting caved in under political pressure driven by the economic concerns of those required to bear the burden of the mandated mitigation—private building owners. Building standards were actually weakened because of the post-disaster process.

The chaos of unplanned, morning-after reactions to disasters, and the role of local politics in framing issues, was evidenced more recently in Princeville, North Carolina, when a vocal group of city leaders fought successfully to have the town rebuilt in the floodplain (Box 4.4).

In the United States, national disaster response is well organized. Within a short time, many federal and non-governmental agencies with extensive resources enter a severely impacted region and provide a wide

> **Box 4.3** Dekle Beach and Oak Island: Post-storm
>   Development Restriction
>
> Development restrictions intersected with a community's desire to
> rebuild in the aftermath of a 1993 winter storm in the small commu-
> nity of Dekle Beach, Florida. In the post-storm damage assessment, it
> was discovered that some destroyed homes had "barnacle-
> encrusted" septic systems and were located on state sovereign sub-
> merged land. In part because of a shifting coastline, but mostly
> because their homes were built before prevailing development
> restrictions, the affected homeowners were barred from redevelop-
> ing because they would be unable to comply with state setback reg-
> ulations. Declaring that "it ain't right" to prevent disaster victims
> from rebuilding, the local state representative introduced legislation
> to waive all environmental regulations interfering with rebuilding.
>   More recently, the post-storm application of coastal develop-
> ment restrictions was documented in Oak Island, North Carolina,
> where severe coastal damage occurred after Hurricane Floyd. The
> administrative rules implementing the state's Coastal Area Manage-
> ment Act require that oceanfront structures be set back a certain dis-
> tance from the first line of stable vegetation. Because of past
> erosion, as well as the effects of the storm on the beach and dune
> system, the vegetation line had shifted and the minimum setback
> was landward of many structures. A coastal management survey
> found that an estimated 91 percent of the beachfront homes on Oak
> Island were within the setback zone. Under state Coastal Resources
> Commission rules, if storm damage exceeds 50 percent of a home's
> value, then the rebuilt home must meet current setback require-
> ments. As a result, several homeowners were not allowed to rebuild.

range of health and social services. There is a tendency, however, for these
service providers to use a top-down approach, ignoring the culture and
capacities of local people. After Hurricane Floyd, for example, many
African-American communities rallied to help neighbors in need. However, according to one report, these outside assistance groups failed to
connect with or value these local resources when they arrived on the
scene.

In the short term, impacted communities are likely to be better
served than before a disaster. Ironically enough, however, these outside
agencies pull out, leaving the local communities weaker than before the
disaster. When working toward more sustainable communities, it is
important for planners to keep an open mind about the meaning of

Box 4.4 The Case of Princeville

Princeville, North Carolina, a historic town founded by former slaves, lies entirely within the floodplain of the Tar River. More important to this story is the connection of people to land and the resounding effort by many of the residents to hold onto a town first chartered and governed by freed slaves—their own ancestors. Their sense of community is encapsulated by the faith that, just as their ancestors prevailed through the floods of this land, they too could persevere and remain the oldest town chartered by African-Americans.

The U.S. Army Corps of Engineers (USACE) built a three-mile-long dike in 1965 to protect the town from a 100-year storm; the dike was overtopped after Hurricane Floyd. Water flooded the town, causing $120 million worth of damage and wiping out or damaging extensively nearly all of the town's 900 homes, the town hall, and the police and fire departments. In the recovery process, local elected officials were eager to rebuild the town at all costs. Federal officials offered funding through the state that was to be limited to the acquisition of damaged homes through the Hazard Mitigation Grant Program (HMGP). Funding limitations through this program became a factor when the town chose to have the Corps of Engineers rebuild the levee. The levee artificially removed these homes from the 100-year floodplain, thus making them ineligible for the HMGP.

The state identified an upland parcel outside the floodplain where the town could be reconstructed. Although many residents favored this move, town officials opposed it, and they prevailed. The USACE constructed a levee to offer a measure of protection to the town, and new homes were constructed in the shadow of the levee. Local officials are pleased with the outcome, but state and federal authorities are concerned that someday the new levee will be overtopped and the homes destroyed. Thus, although political leadership resulted in preservation of the town in its original location, that same leadership may have led individuals to select a less secure mitigation option, rather than rebuilding their homes on higher ground.

One of the many buildings in Princeville that were not strapped to their foundations. It floated on top of the family truck during the flooding—both a total loss.

Source: Dave Gatley/FEMA News Photo.

"community," looking beyond political boundaries to involve residents, local officials, the public sector, the private sector, and nonprofit agencies—indeed, all the stakeholders of a socially defined region (Esnard 2001). Disaster planners are learning that it is essential to work with local agencies and organizations, to build lasting capacity and communities that are more disaster-resilient.

ECONOMIC INSTITUTIONS

The destruction of buildings and infrastructure is likely to have economic impacts that extend far beyond the direct costs associated with repairing or rebuilding. Many economic enterprises will be temporarily suspended; some may become insolvent and permanently lost to the community. Indeed, a community's economic profile is likely to be permanently altered.

When commercial property is damaged, not only are services and products lost to the community, but jobs are also lost and the tax base is reduced. If businesses are forced to remain closed for long periods, the economic effects on the individual enterprises, as well as the community

Figure 4.2 Destroyed businesses have multiplier effects on community difficulties. Photo by Liz Roll/ FEMA News Photo.

as a whole, can be devastating. Even when a particular business is not directly affected, infrastructure damage, such as the loss of utilities and roads, can cause interruptions for long periods (Box 4.5).

The first major effort to assemble all direct economic cost data for an earthquake was undertaken after the Northridge earthquake in California. Federal and state costs, as well as insured losses and costs to repair damaged lifelines (water and electricity), exceeded $24 billion (Eguchi et al. 1996). However, Eguchi and associates estimated that these costs represented only about half of the total losses. The other costs consisted of uninsured losses, including deductibles and self-insured business and commercial losses.

The economic losses are apt to be large even in less urban areas. In a study of the potential physical and human consequences if a major earthquake were to occur in the New Madrid fault area (Shelby County/ Memphis, Tennessee), Litan et al. (1992) estimated that the temporary losses in economic output stemming from damage to workplaces could be as much as $7.6 billion, based on the magnitude of unemployment and the accompanying losses in wages, profits, and indirect "multiplier" effects.

Flooding from hurricanes Dennis and Floyd in eastern North Carolina in 1999 affected about 60,000 businesses, resulting in more than $955 million in business losses (Delia 2001). The average repair cost for physical damage was about $40,000 per business, with an average revenue loss of nearly $80,000.

Box 4.5   Far-Reaching Impacts of Infrastructure Damage

In 1993, the Mississippi River flooded the Des Moines Water Works in Iowa. The plant was out of operation for 12 days, and the water was unsafe for drinking for another 7 days. Businesses and government offices were forced to close because of a lack of fire protection; bottled water and portable toilets had to be provided to residents. More businesses in the city suspended operations because of the loss of electricity, water, and sewer and wastewater services than because of a lack of customers or employee access (Interagency Floodplain Management Review Committee 1994). Similarly, when Hurricane Floyd flooded a single Bell Atlantic building in New Jersey, telephone service was cut to about 1 million local customers and 8,000 automated teller machines throughout the country (Esnard 2001).

Recovery tends to be most difficult for small, privately owned businesses. According to an expert assisting in North Carolina's recovery, about 50 percent of the smaller or newer businesses may never recover (Fitts 2001). For larger businesses with longer records of accomplishment, Fitts expected four out of six to recover. About 5,000 families were expected to sell their farms. In general, many small, local businesses are lost after a major event. "The first businesses reopening after Hurricane Andrew were almost exclusively national fast-food franchises and retail chain outlets. . . . In contrast to small owner-operated businesses, they could access multinational and national capital resources to quickly get back in business" (Dash et al. 1997, p. 215).

Figure 4.3 Many homes and businesses suffered extensive damage from Hurricane Andrew, one of the most destructive hurricanes ever recorded in the United States. *Source*: FEMA News Photo.

There are economic winners and losers in any major disaster. Businesses associated with preparation and recovery activities, such as building material suppliers, roofers, and appliance and furniture stores, are likely to have more business than they can handle and may make a handsome profit as a result of a disaster, or even the threat of one. Large building supply outlets, such as Home Depot, routinely warehouse plywood, generators, and other materials needed for hurricane response and recovery. They can send them quickly to a targeted region, extend store hours, and otherwise respond to the increased demand.

After a high-impact hazard event, there is an influx of new resources into the community as public and private organizations respond and insurance payments are made. Construction materials are in heavy demand, and their prices may increase because of shortages and the many immediate needs. Household products and personal property need to be replaced. Sales tax revenues are likely to soar during the rebuilding period, providing a windfall to local and state governments.

Less is known about longer-term economic impacts on a severely affected area. Although most relocation from damaged homes is temporary, sometimes a shop's customer base shrinks when people decide to remain in the new area or seek opportunities elsewhere. Social and economic trends already under way can be hastened by a major disaster (Peacock and Morrow 2000). In the year following Hurricane Andrew, at least 50,000 people moved out of south Dade County permanently, accelerating "Anglo" flight into less-Hispanic Broward County to the north and permanently changing daily commuting patterns into downtown Miami. Another major economic blow was the premature closing of largely destroyed Homestead Air Force Base. Not only were the base personnel and their families lost to the region, but many military retirees left when military facilities and services were no longer available. Although the base eventually might have been closed anyway, the hurricane hastened its demise.

Entire sectors of a local economy can be permanently changed. The floods associated with Hurricane Floyd profoundly affected hog farming and associated waste treatment facilities in North Carolina, drawing attention to the environmental impacts of this industry. Hurricane Floyd dumped large amounts of rainfall onto the principal hog-growing areas of eastern North Carolina, flooding part or all of many swine farms and their waste treatment systems. Initial estimates varied wildly, but one official estimate of the numbers of animals killed included 30,500 hogs,

Figure 4.4   Though 30 cows drowned from flooding caused by Hurricane Irene at the W.D. Dairy in Broward County, Florida, the owners of the dairy avoided a major loss by having raised the feeding areas, where about 1,700 cows graze, above the floodplain. *Source*: FEMA News Photo/G. Mathieson.

2.2 million chickens, 737,000 turkeys, and 880 cattle (Scwhab 2000). At least 300 hog waste treatment systems were known to be adversely affected, of which at least 180 were located in the 100-year floodplain. At least 26 hog waste lagoons were known to have ruptured.

PRIVATE SECTOR INVOLVEMENT

Specific information on how private sector involvement has reduced (or can be a factor in reducing) community vulnerability is scarce. Recent studies have called for public/private partnerships to address disaster preparedness, but not enough is known about the particular mechanisms that could be used to mitigate not only the businesses themselves, but also the larger community. The Heinz Center (2000b) articulated a need to ensure that community-based planning models and risk reduction programs address business vulnerability. Maiolo and Stone (2001), as part of their Hurricane Floyd after-action review, recommended public education programs to prepare small business owners for natural hazards, urging emergency managers to engage the private sector.

The traditional approach to business protection looks to protecting or strengthening the place of business operations. Activities include planning for continuity of operations, structural assessments, and physical retrofits. Unfortunately, businesses often have looked at the impact on their employees as an afterthought. A business can be as secure as Fort Knox, but if employees cannot make it to work, the bottom line will be affected. Businesses can reduce community vulnerability by actively recognizing the needs of their employees; pressuring other businesses, including their suppliers, to take disaster loss reduction seriously; and actively coordinating with local governments in disaster planning and response.

It is critical that public outreach programs targeting the private sector underscore the positive role that businesses can play in reducing social, as well as economic, vulnerability. Examples of possible actions include using a business for public education information dissemination on hazards; allowing employees time off to take measures to protect their homes; including on-site shelter space for family members of employees required to stay at the workplace during a hazard event; and providing pre- and post-disaster counseling and referral for insurance, reconstruction matters, and physical and mental health issues (Box 4.6).

A creative way for businesses to serve as catalysts in strengthening communities is through interactions with other businesses. Some require their distributors and suppliers to have continuity-of-operations plans. This "business to business" self-policing on loss reduction builds momentum without relying on government intervention. An excellent example of this is STOP (Strategically Targeted Outreach Program). Developed in Southern California after the Loma Prieta earthquake, this volunteer organization of culturally diverse business leaders reaches out to small business owners, particularly in minority communities, to assist in the development of emergency response and business continuity plans, including a requirement that key vendors and suppliers have such plans as part of future contracts.

Box 4.6 One Business Making a Difference

J.M. Family Enterprise is the Southeast's largest Toyota distributorship. Headquartered in Deerfield Beach, Florida, this company has taken a proactive role in exploring and implementing both traditional and creative disaster loss reduction activities. In terms of traditional systems and organization, J.M. Family has a corporate continuity planning function that is staffed and includes company-wide exercises. The company conducted a facility-wide assessment and performed benefit–cost based retrofits on selected structures. It is an active member in the local Chamber of Commerce and a charter member of a city-organized disaster business alliance.

The area in which J.M. Family has been creative, and has worked actively to reduce social vulnerability, is community-based disaster loss reduction. Examples of these activities include mentoring area businesses in developing disaster continuity plans; hosting an annual Hurricane Expo for employees; and sponsoring community-wide outreach events, including the city's popular Beach Blowout/Hurricane Awareness day. The company donated resources to build the local Boys and Girls Club—with disaster-resilient windows and construction techniques. The philanthropic activities of the company's founder include a recent project to build an automotive-repair training center for at-risk youth. According to the economic development coordinator for the city of Deerfield Beach, these "nontraditional" social commitments play an important role in reducing social vulnerability and may reduce economic recovery time (Baia 2001).

Direct benefits can accrue to businesses through coordination with the government on disaster-related issues. Such benefits include improved access to information before, during, and after an event; promotion of cross-sector networking in which business leaders get to know the public sector leaders charged with making critical response and recovery decisions; eased re-entry into their business and thus eased recovery; and good public relations from becoming known as a business with a "social commitment" to the community. Government intervention may be required to create incentives for the private sector, particularly banks and insurers, to offer products to reduce social vulnerability or target socially vulnerable populations (Box 4.7).

After Florida's post–Hurricane Andrew insurance crisis, the state commissioner of insurance required certain firms with large, profitable automotive insurance businesses to offer more-risky homeowners'

Box 4.7 Promoting Mitigation Equity

Incentives may be required to promote socially responsible behavior by the insurance and banking industries in an effort to reduce community-wide social vulnerability. The Community Reinvestment Act (CRA, 12 U.S.C. 2901) was passed to require banks and other lending institutions to serve all clients in their service areas, combating racial discrimination in lending patterns.

The CRA can serve as a model for the type of regulatory tools that may be needed to ensure that banks offer loans for retrofitting in coastal hazard areas and that insurance companies offer affordable homeowners protection and include continuity of operations coverage in business insurance policies. Such incentives could reduce "redlining"—pricing the socially vulnerable out of favorable mortgages and adequate insurance.

---

property and casualty insurance as a condition of doing business in the state. Just as safe and affordable housing is a key to reducing social vulnerability, so too is an insurance "safety net" that is available to all consumers at an affordable price. The social benefit of this type of safety net likely outweighs any actuarial unsoundness. Banks can play a role by offering loan products to homeowners and businesses at reasonable rates to conduct structural assessments and retrofits. By promoting affordable, pre-disaster retrofitting of structures on which mortgages are held, the banking industry can reduce its potential for loss through foreclosure on damaged or destroyed structures.

NEED FOR PRIVATE–PUBLIC PARTNERSHIPS

There is a need to bring together interested parties from the private sector, public interest groups, regulatory agencies and other governmental organizations, and the public to develop mitigation strategies. Partnerships are likely to lead to more viable solutions than would be developed by any of these groups working independently (Box 4.8).

Even with financial incentives for private-sector action, government regulations and standards may be needed to cover contingencies. In the case of an earthquake, a building collapse can break a gas pipeline and cause a major fire, damaging property not affected by the earthquake directly, and

Box 4.8 Public-Private Partnership Example

To illustrate how a private–public partnership would work, suppose an industrial firm can spend $15,000 to make its plant more hurricane resistant, potentially saving $200,000 in property damage from a severe storm that has an annual probability of 1/100. In this case the expected reduction in annual damage from the investment is $2,000 (i.e., 1/100 * $200,000), so an insurer could reduce its premium to the firm by approximately this amount. In this case, the $15,000 investment would not pay for itself in the 2- to 5-year payback period often required by the firm's management.

How could the managers be encouraged to make this investment? Insurers and banks can work together to offer incentives to purchase protection in the form of loans. If a 20-year loan with an interest rate of 10% were offered on the market, the firm would now face an annual loan payment of $1,700 coupled with an annual $2,000 reduction in its insurance premium. This means the firm comes out ahead by $300 per year, the bank earns a reasonable interest rate, and the insurers have a reduced chance of experiencing large claims from disasters by encouraging their policyholders to adopt loss reduction measures (Kunreuther 2002a).

these indirect losses are not likely to be covered by the firm's insurance policy. A well-enforced building code that requires the adoption of cost-effective mitigation measures would help reduce risks and the need for financial assistance for those who otherwise would incur uninsured losses.

CHALLENGES FACING THE INSURANCE INDUSTRY

The insurance industry plays a key role in economic development. Until recently, overbuilding and high real-estate prices in the hurricane-prone Atlantic and Gulf coast areas have been facilitated by relatively inexpensive and readily available property insurance. Commercial development has followed population movement to coastal areas, and this trend has increased the potential economic losses from natural hazards.

At the same time, the insurance industry plays a key role in providing relief to victims after a disaster and in aiding recovery. This was evident in the aftermath of the two most severe natural disasters in recent years, Hurricane Andrew and the Northridge earthquake. Total damage from Hurricane Andrew was estimated at nearly $30 billion, with $15.5 billion in insurance payouts. Similarly, for the 1994 Northridge earthquake, for which total damage was estimated at $44 billion (Eguchi et al. 1996), private insurers paid out almost $13 billion in claims (Institute for Business and Home Safety 1998). The insured losses for Hurricane Floyd were $1.8 billion (Insurance Services Office 2000).

     Recovery is largely dependent on the extent to which property is insured and claims payments are made promptly. If the destruction is especially extensive, some insurers become insolvent, placing additional financial burdens on other insurers that are assessed by the state's insurance guaranty fund to pay the losses of the defunct companies up to the maximum provided by law. Losses from Hurricane Andrew triggered the failure of nine small and medium-sized insurers (Box 4.9).

Box 4.9 The Hurricane Andrew Insurance Crisis

The case of Hurricane Andrew highlights the challenges facing the entire insurance sector, as well as the long-term impacts on a community. More than 28,000 homes were destroyed, an additional 107,380 homes were damaged, and 180,000 people were left homeless (Gallagher 1993). The disaster caused an estimated $15.5 billion in insured residential and personal property losses.

     The large number of homeowners' claims was due to damage to contents and other covered items for owner- and non-owner-occupied structures. Almost 12,000 mobile home claims were made, many involving total loss of the home and its contents (IIPLR and IRC 1995). Commercial insurance claims covering property damage, inventory loss, and loss of use were triggered by the total destruction of, or damage to, 82,000 businesses. The loss of power to 1.4 million residents and the loss of telephone service to some 80,000 locations resulted in the interruption of business activities, loss of electronic records, and spoilage of food (Gallagher 1993).

     Hurricane Andrew placed an enormous burden on the insurance industry. Nine property/casualty insurance companies became insolvent as a direct result of this disaster. A tenth company became insolvent because of the state guaranty fund's post-Andrew assessments. Insolvencies also contributed to problems with the availability of property insurance after Andrew. Policyholders with damaged property were unable to purchase a policy because most insurers do not accept damaged property under a new policy (Lecomte and Gahagan 1998).

Some companies contend they are facing an excessive risk of insolvency due to high concentrations of catastrophe exposures and insufficient reinsurance. The insurance industry was caught off guard by losses following Hurricane Andrew and the Northridge earthquake and significantly underestimated the amount of eventual claims. As a result, insurers prudently have sought to decrease their exposure and increase their rates substantially. To avoid future catastrophic losses, some companies have discontinued coverage in high-risk areas. The terrorist acts of September 11, 2001, raised this issue in a graphic way, with the insurance and reinsurance industries claiming they could not provide coverage against terrorism unless they had some protection from the federal government. Although there was considerable pressure by insurers and re-insurers for the government to provide some type of federal protection against large losses from terrorism, Congress did not pass any legislation at the end of its December 2001 session. As a result, there has been limited terrorism insurance provided on the market. When coverage has been offered, the amount of protection is more limited and more expensive since the September 11 terrorist attacks (Kunreuther 2002b). Property owners in coastal areas are experiencing greater difficulty than before in acquiring insurance and are paying considerably more for it. Consumers have found it difficult to adapt to rapid and severe changes in insurance market conditions.

On a more positive note, new scientific studies, engineering analyses, and advances in information technology offer opportunities to improve estimates of the risks and potential losses of future disasters. More sophisticated risk assessments have reduced the uncertainty associated with estimating the probabilities that earthquakes and hurricanes of various intensities and magnitudes will occur in specific regions. Engineering studies, building on the experience of past disasters, have provided new information on how structures perform under the stress of natural forces. The development of faster and more powerful computers enables these data to be combined in ways that were impossible even five years ago. These new developments are expected to provide a more complete picture of property at risk so that insurers can specify more accurately premiums that reflect their expected future losses (Kunreuther and Roth 1998).

EDUCATIONAL AND CULTURAL INSTITUTIONS

The educational system is one of the first institutional sectors affected when hazards threaten or batter a community. School buildings are often pressed into service as community shelters, placing extra burdens on school personnel and interfering with regular school programs. After a major disaster, the facilities may be used for short-term temporary housing even when schools are closed because of damage. The protection of children is important to any community. Thus, it would seem logical for mitigation projects that "harden" schools against natural disasters to have high priority for use as shelters. There have been a number of programs directed at making schools and daycare centers safer, including the Organization of American States Natural Hazards Project directed at school vulnerability reduction (see www.oas.org/nhp).

From the standpoint of children and families, the aftermath of a disaster is a particularly difficult time for schools to be closed. Damaged homes and neighborhoods are dangerous and depressing places. Children are often left with no safe place to play when yards, playgrounds, and recreational programs are lost; no one to play with when playmates and friends are forced to relocate; and a lack of supervision and attention when parents are too busy dealing with survival and rebuilding issues. Social service agencies recognize the potential for inadequate parenting, even child abuse, as overburdened parents deal with bored children in damaged or destroyed homes and neighborhoods.

Schools are more than centers of education. In American culture, they define neighborhoods, binding parents and other citizens together around community concerns and activities. They serve as recreation centers, community meeting places, and places of employment. The closing of a local school is highly disruptive to social networks and, if it becomes permanent, can rob a neighborhood of its identity and cohesion. One of the most dramatic impacts on a severely affected community occurs when a school is closed for a long time, maybe even permanently, because of regional depopulation. Similarly, damage to colleges and universities can result in losses of educational time as well as employment and regional business opportunities.

Getting schools reopened quickly has been identified as an important step toward rebuilding a community as a whole (Provenzo and Fradd 1995). Largely because of repairs completed by the military, the Miami–Dade public school system opened within two weeks after Hurricane Andrew, although some schools were closed for months, and several for an entire year. Teaching is difficult in damaged buildings and neighborhoods, especially when the teachers themselves are going through major trauma, but it can be the best compromise for children and families dealing with the results of a major disaster.

The long-term effects of major disasters on the education and development of children is an under-studied area. More is known about the psychological effects, including post-traumatic stress (Vernberg et al. 1996, Jones et al. 1993, Boore and Aptekar 1990), and the effects of stress on children's memories of a natural disaster (Parker et al. 1997). The shock of being uprooted and moved to a new school, even temporarily, can be particularly traumatic if it occurs at a critical developmental time, such as the senior year in high school, with its college preparation and graduation festivities (Marks 1993).

Childcare providers are likely to be unable to function after a disaster. Day care centers may be damaged or unsafe. Home-based providers with damaged homes and pressing demands from their own families may not be able to take care of clients' children. Yet, this largely informal economic sector is vital to the functioning of many families and businesses; without childcare, many parents cannot report to work. Similarly, day care programs for dependent adults provide essential services that may be disrupted or lost.

Leisure and recreational programs usually cease after a major disaster. Parks may be destroyed and staff members diverted to other duties. Parent volunteers are busy putting their own lives in order; school athletic and extracurricular programs are placed on hold; public entertainment facilities, such as theaters and skating rinks, are closed. In short, there may be little or nothing constructive for children to do in their spare time—and they may have more of it than usual. Anecdotal information from authorities tied increased gang activity in the years following Hurricane Andrew to the neglect of teenagers by parents and the community

Figure 4.5 Children can express the trauma of a disaster with artwork, as these children have here. *Source:* FEMA News Photo.

during the long recovery period (Mainster 1998). One solution is to keep children occupied in reconstruction activities. Acknowledging the positive effects of involving children in disaster-related activities, including cleanup and recovery, FEMA has developed a Web site on the topic (www.fema.gov/kids).

Religious organizations are seriously affected when disaster strikes. A local church or synagogue may be the first place the community turns to for immediate help. The legacy of every disaster includes stories about individual churches and religious leaders who rose to the forefront to respond to community needs, often with little outside help. Local churches are sources of numerous humanitarian efforts, providing consolation, relief supplies, and counseling. Their mission often extends beyond their membership, reaching throughout the area. Yet, these demands come at a time when these organizations may be weakened themselves, operating in damaged facilities with fewer workers than usual. Membership and donor bases shrink when families are forced to relocate.

Local social service agencies do not have the resources to cope with the overwhelming needs that follow a major impact. This can be

Figure 4.6 These children in Glenville, Deleware, help with clean-up activities after a flood. *Source*: Andrea Booher/FEMA News Photos.

especially true in previously underserved, often poor and minority, communities. This is another aspect of community life in which a disaster is likely to reveal preexisting weaknesses. Occupational burnout among service providers is also common in the case of long, difficult recovery periods.

Most of the cultural organizations and activities defining communities are likely to suffer after a disaster. Museums, art shows, and other cultural events are low funding priorities compared to more pressing needs. They may lose patrons and volunteers as other priorities take precedence. Libraries can be destroyed easily; even slight roof damage can wreak havoc on collections (Box 4.10).

People need activities to bring them together during what can be a very isolating experience. Reopening libraries and other civic centers has important morale-building as well as utilitarian value. Continuing cultural events, such as parades and festivals, during difficult reconstruction periods is important in helping communities regain identity and pride. Recent work analyzing cultural artifacts associated with disasters, such as the quilts women sometimes make about disaster experiences, has drawn attention to this neglected area of human response (Enarson 2000).

Box 4.10 Libraries and Disasters

When Hurricane Hugo hit the island of St. Croix in the U.S. Virgin Islands in 1989, it destroyed the only two libraries on the island. The public library in Christiansted was flooded by storm surge, and the library at the University of the Virgin Islands lost most of its roof to the winds. For months thereafter, passersby often saw books lying in the sun to dry as librarians tried to salvage as many as possible.

After Hurricane Andrew, there was no public library serving the south Miami–Dade area, and the library at Homestead Senior High was closed; students had no library services available for more than a year.

The importance of public libraries has dwindled in the American psyche, as evidenced by reduced funding in most communities. Although they tend to be severely affected when coastal hazards hit, libraries seldom receive sufficient assistance to reduce their losses and restart their services in a timely manner. Yet, they can be key factors in community rebuilding by offering practical resources, meeting places, and free leisure activities.

FAMILY AND SOCIAL RELATIONSHIPS

Families are where the "rubber meets the road" when it comes to disaster response. Regardless of geography or culture, most people experience and are most affected by a hazard event as members of households. More specifically, it is families, defined as the primary set of relationships and obligations that bind most households together, where most disaster-related decisions are made, where mitigation, evacuation, and other response actions are taken, and where the results are experienced.

Even in post-industrial societies, families continue to bear major responsibility for caring for the most vulnerable segments of society— dependent children, the ill, the handicapped, and the elderly. "The family is the unit through which most people meet their day-to-day needs. To the extent that the family is disrupted or separated by disaster, the coping capacity of its individual members is weakened" (Wiest et al. 1994). In addition, as previously discussed, within the family, domestic work remains almost exclusively the responsibility of women. At no time is this more evident than when disaster strikes (Enarson and Morrow 1997).

Women's Role in Household and Community Response

There is a gender dimension to the effects and responses associated with any social event, particularly one of the magnitude of a disaster. "In any society in which elaborate gender domains are constructed, then both hazards and relief measures will be 'gendered' with different consequences for men and women" (Shaw 1989, p. 13). To truly understand the ability of a household to respond, one needs to understand its patterns of domestic labor and decision making.

Although experiences vary with class, culture, and situation, women continue to be responsible for most family and domestic work, even when they participate in the formal labor force (Hochschild 1989). Moreover, the number of women bearing total responsibility for households has increased dramatically. In the United States, female-headed families and female-alone units now make up over 29 percent of all households (U.S. Bureau of the Census 2000), and among minorities and the elderly, the proportion is even higher. About 49 percent of black family households are headed by women, and 40 percent of elderly women live alone.

The greater vulnerability of women to any disaster, including coastal hazards, stems not so much from biology as from the cultural, political, and economic structures that affect the conditions of their everyday lives. It is estimated that women and children make up 70 to 80 percent of those needing assistance after most disasters (League of Red Cross and Red Crescent Societies 1991). Along the U.S. coastlines live hundreds of thousands of women and their families who are poor, and/or marginalized, and thus particularly vulnerable to coastal hazards. Yet, when disaster strikes, the needs of women and children tend to be low priorities (Enarson and Morrow 1998).

The aim here is not to portray women as victims only, because they are also instrumental at every level of disaster response, from the individual household level to national organizations. In addition to assuming primary responsibility for the care of family members, women form the core of many, if not most, U.S. community disaster volunteer programs. Women's caregiving work extends into the paid workforce, where they are found disproportionately in health, education, and social service organizations. Yet, even in occupations dominated by women, they rarely hold top management positions (Acker 1991). As an example, women are

Figure 4.7 Cleanup begins after Hurricane Floyd in Franklin, Virginia as two parishioners clean the Franklin Baptist Church, which had been flooded to a depth of some 15 feet. *Source:* Liz Roll/FEMA News Photo.

only now beginning to break into the field of emergency management (Wilson 1999). Although women play crucial public and private roles, their voices are largely absent in public and private policymaking, including decisions about disaster response and recovery. One way to improve disaster services to families is to use the resources of women more effectively (for example, by hiring and including women at decision-making levels in emergency management and disaster response planning).

FAMILIES AND DISASTER RESPONSE

Families and households are not always synonymous. Yet, even when people living together are not related by blood or marriage, it is still highly likely that they will involve each other when deciding whether to purchase flood insurance or shutters, whether to evacuate and where, and how to meet household needs throughout the recovery process. On the other hand, many kin-based activities extend beyond individual households, and this is especially evident in times of crisis. There is a growing body of evidence that many relatives living outside households are involved in disaster decisions and actions. Relatives figured heavily in disaster-related activities in South Florida in response to Hurricane Andrew, including assistance with preparation, cleanup, sheltering, and relocation (Morrow 1997), and this was particularly true for minority and poor families.

As discussed in earlier chapters, certain attributes associated with gender, race/ethnicity, social class, and household composition affect each household's vulnerability and ability to respond. Taken together, these characteristics place many U.S. households at risk (Table 4.1). These are not mutually exclusive categories and, in fact, are likely to be found intersecting in ways that magnify the vulnerability of many households, such as an elderly minority woman living alone.

Some households are better prepared—physically, economically, and socially—than others to deal with the impact of a major disaster (Bolin 1985). However, there are many ways in which strong families can be threatened, even destroyed, by the painful experience of a direct impact and lengthy recovery period.

The single largest economic asset of most families is the equity in their homes; thus, widespread destruction means the potential for financial ruin is high. Moreover, a home is more than just a structure, but

Table 4.1 Vulnerable Types of U.S. Households

Type of Household	Percent of Total[a]
Poor (below poverty level)	11.3
Female-headed	
With children under 18	7.2
Living alone	12.2
Disabled	19.7[b]
Elderly (over 65)	9.2
Racial Minority	32.9
Non-family	31.9
Renters	33.8

Source: U.S. Census 2000, www.census.gov.
[a] The numbers add up to more than 100 because a household can fall into more than one category.
[b] 1997 American with Disabilities Act [data for individuals (3.8 percent need personal assistance)].

"where the heart is." When family housing is damaged or destroyed, the loss is profoundly felt. Even if the uninsured losses turn out to be minor, people are likely to suffer in many ways during long recovery periods.

The stress takes its toll at the most intimate level—in the family. There is evidence that all family relationships become more stressful, from those between partners to those between parent and child and among relatives, neighbors, and friends (Morrow 1997). The effect can be especially acute on marital relationships (Davis and Ender 1999), sometimes increasing the incidence of domestic violence (Fothergill 1999, Wilson et al. 1998).

Some ways in which families can be affected are summarized in Table 4.2. In the end, a family can be destroyed by the trauma and stress—or it can emerge stronger from the experience.

SOME FAMILIES AND COMMUNITIES EMERGE MORE RESILIENT

No research has been done on the long-term effects of major disasters on families. However, there is ample evidence that recovery periods are difficult for individuals and their families. There is a tendency in U.S. culture to consider the well-being of children and families to be a private matter, outside public responsibility. After a disaster, parents are expected to

Table 4.2   Potential Effects of Disasters on Families

Physical	Loss of family members
	Loss of friends
	Destroyed or damaged homes
	Loss of possessions, including personal mementos
	Loss of environment and tools for everyday living
	Temporary or permanent dislocation
	Longer commutes to work or school
	Loss of local businesses and services
	Loss of schools and recreational programs
Economic	Uninsured home and property losses
	Temporary or permanent loss of employment
	Increased transportation costs
	Higher living costs
Social	Loss of neighborhood
	Loss of social networks
	Loss of social institutions and services
Emotional or psychological	Role overload, conflict
	Overworked parents and bored children
	Stress in intimate and partner relationships
	Family violence, including child abuse
	Emotional and psychological problems
	Behavioral problems in children

continue protecting, caring for, and nurturing their families. The demands can be unrealistic, and, more than before, a strong community support system is needed to help families cope.

In times of disaster, some families do better than others. Some actually emerge stronger because of the experience. Several factors have been associated with resilience (Table 4.3). Some of these, such as strong emotional ties, sound economic base, relative gender equality, stable family and social networks, and good community integration, are associated with strong families in general. Others speak more to the disaster situation, such as having a high ratio of productive adults to dependents, being well informed about hazards, and having completed mitigation initiatives.

Like families, some communities are more disaster-resilient than others. Positive community-level factors include a stable and strong economic base; relative social and economic equality; strong community

Table 4.3   Factors Associated with Disaster Resiliency

Family	Strong emotional ties
	Sound economic base
	Stable family and/or social networks
	Well integrated into the community
	Relative gender equality and sharing of household tasks
	High ratio of productive adults to dependents
	Well-informed about hazards
	Mitigation initiatives in place
Community	Strong economic base
	Relative economic and racial equality
	Strong community institutions
	Effective government, including good land use and zoning
	Good family support systems (day care, counseling, recreational programs)
	Women caregivers and their needs integrated into planning and programs
	Effective planning for community development that includes mitigation

Source: Esnard 2001.

institutions; and effective government that understands the risk and miti-gates against it, especially in long-term activities such as land use, zoning, and building codes (Esnard 2001). Effective policy planning includes all constituencies and effectively uses the expertise of women and minorities at all levels. Further, strong communities have good heath and social ser-vices before hazards strike, and plans in place to prevent service interrup-tion. Such communities also have strong mitigation programs, including neighborhood-level initiatives.

Disaster-resilient communities are sustainable communities—and good places to live. Most community planners have a good under-standing of the people who make up the community, including their strengths as well as weaknesses. Marshaling community resources to address social and economic root causes of vulnerability is the long-term answer to the question of how best to meet the challenges of coastal haz-ards. Post-disaster reconstruction can provide a unique opportunity to address social and economic inequalities and build stronger communities. Bolin and Stanford (1998) cite Piru, California, after the Northridge earthquake as one example of a community that recognized the needs of its residents and included affordable housing in redevelopment plans.

Social institutions and their social networks define a population as a community. The extent to which they function effectively largely determines disaster resilience. The quality and availability of housing, education, health and social services, recreation, cultural and religious activities, employment, transportation, public safety are all factors that affect disaster resistance—and that also enhances the quality of everyday life in a community (Geis 2000). The long-term protection and sustenance of these resources for all the citizens of a community is at the heart of good mitigation and response planning.

CONCLUSIONS AND RECOMMENDATIONS

Most governments, particularly at the local level, are not prepared to deal adequately with a coastal disaster. Even when they are prepared to handle immediate emergency needs, most have not planned for recovery. This can accentuate pain and suffering, prolong recovery, create political fallout, and result in the rebuilding of unsafe communities.

- **Governments at all levels of jurisdiction should have all-hazard disaster plans in place, including recovery plans with mitigation measures for rebuilding safer communities. Disaster planning should be developed in partnership with all interested parties and should cut across political boundaries to serve the citizens of a region.**

After an event, economic losses to the business community can be devastating to individual enterprises, especially small local businesses, and to the economy and quality of life in the community as a whole.

- **Public and private initiatives and programs to promote effective disaster planning in the business sector, particularly for small, local businesses, should be expanded. Business disaster plans should include initiatives to assist employees and their families in preparing and responding in a timely manner. Federal, state, and local initiatives should include public–private partnerships and use a variety of means, including insurance, building codes and regulations, loans, subsidies, and economic incentives, to improve community economic resilience to hazards.**

Public concern and funding related to the care and nurturance of children tends to be limited, a reality that becomes particularly noticeable after a major disaster, when children's needs tend to be considered low priority compared to other concerns, such as economic interests. Little is known about the long-term developmental and behavioral effects on children when a community, including its educational and cultural institutions, fails to address the needs of children and youth adequately during long disaster recovery periods.

■ **Every level of jurisdiction should make the needs of children and youth a higher priority throughout all stages of disaster response. Local plans and federal response programs should be in place to assist organizations that serve children (educational, child care, recreational, cultural, health and social services agencies) in resuming operations quickly. Although schools may need to be used as temporary shelters, they should not be used as longer-term housing for dislocated victims. Parks and recreational programs provide children with diversions from damaged homes and stressed families, leading to safer communities. The need for additional teacher assistants, social workers, and other support services for parents and educators should be anticipated as part of community disaster planning. Child care programs, including informal services, should receive high priority in community rebuilding activities. More research is needed on the long-term effects of disasters on child development and learning.**

Cultural and social institutions are the heart of a community. When they are disrupted, not only are services unavailable, but communities lose much of their identity and definition. Museums, art shows, and other cultural and social events tend to be low priorities after a disaster, yet they serve important social, psychological, and educational functions.

■ **Local organizations should be encouraged to hold cultural and social events throughout recovery periods. These events facilitate social networks, provide an important respite from recovery activities, serve as venues for distributing or gathering community information, help combat depression, and serve to bind communities together.**

When disaster strikes, community religious and service organizations are apt to be crippled, losing donors and volunteers at a time when they are most needed. In the United States, nonprofit organizations are well organized to enter a community to assist with recovery needs. However, they tend to operate independently, failing to work through local groups. This can reduce the effectiveness of their services, as well as undermine local organizations.

▪ Governmental and nongovernmental response groups coming into a community to assist with relief and recovery should work through local churches, organizations and agencies, building their capacity rather than supplanting it. Actively working with community-based organizations can reveal hidden vulnerability.

The responsibility for caring for dependent members of society, especially children and the elderly, rests almost entirely upon families—and within families, most often upon women. It is within these same family units that most disaster-related decisions and actions occur. Although women provide the bulk of caregiving, for cultural and historical reasons they often lack the economic resources and personal autonomy needed for family preparation and recovery. Households headed by women are among the poorest and most marginalized, and these high-risk households are especially prevalent in coastal communities.

▪ One way to reduce the vulnerability of coastal populations is to adopt disaster-related policies and practices that better reflect an understanding of the daily circumstances of families. Rigid definitions of what constitutes a family should be avoided when qualifying families for assistance. Effective family services include child care at disaster application centers; outreach programs for those without private transportation; policies to facilitate kinship networks of assistance; and programs to deal with family stress, conflict, and violence. A major step toward improving services to families, and improving disaster response in general, would be to use the resources of the nation's women more effectively at all levels of disaster planning and response. This includes hiring and including more women at decision-making levels in emergency management and disaster response planning; creating participatory processes to help build inclusiveness of gender, age, race, and those with disabilities into consensus-building public meetings, discussions, and workshops related to mitigation and disaster response.

In summary, the human community turns a hazard into a disaster. As the coasts become increasingly populated, more and more people are placed in harm's way. Thus far, science has not found effective ways to reduce most hazards. Therefore, citizens must look to strengthening communities. Building safer buildings and strengthening infrastructure are important steps, but it is the manner in which *societies* are built that largely determines disaster resilience. A vital part of effective disaster planning—whether for mitigation, preparation, response or recovery—is an understanding of the people and institutions that make up each community, including their strengths and their weaknesses, as a basis for developing policies, programs, and practices to protect them. In the end, it is human decisions related to such matters as land use planning and community priorities that will build stronger, safer, and better communities.

APPENDIXES

APPENDIX A

GLOSSARY

Atmospheric pressure is the pressure exerted by the atmosphere at a given point. It can be measured in several ways: in millibars, inches, or millimeters of mercury (Hg). It is also known as barometric pressure.

Beach is the zone of unconsolidated material that extends landward from the water line to the place where there is marked change in material or physiographic form, or to the line of permanent vegetation. The beach includes foreshore and backshore.

Beach nourishment is the process of replenishing a beach. It may occur naturally by longshore transport, or artificially by deposition of dredged materials.

Bluff is a high, steep bank or cliff.

Chronic hazard is an enduring or recurring hazard, such as beach, dune, and bluff erosion; gradual weathering of sea cliffs; and flooding of low-lying lands during major storms.

Coast is a strip of land of indefinite width that extends from the shoreline inland to the first major change in terrain features.

Coastal county is defined as having (1) at least 15 percent of its total land area within the nation's coastal watershed, or (2) a portion of its land accounting for at least 15 percent of a coastal cataloging unit. The United States has 673 coastal counties.

Coastal zone is all U.S. waters subject to the tide; U.S. waters of the Great Lakes; specified ports and harbors on inland rivers; waters that are navigable by deep-draft vessels, including the contiguous zone and parts of the high seas; and the land surface or land substrata, groundwater, and ambient air proximal to those waters.

Coastline   is, technically, the line that forms the boundary between the coast and the shore, or, commonly, the line that forms the boundary between the land and the water.

Depression,   in meteorology, is another name for an area of low pressure, a low, or trough. It also applies to a stage of tropical cyclone development, known as a tropical depression to distinguish it from other synoptic features.

Dunes   are ridges or mounds of loose, wind-blown material, usually sand.

Ecosystem   is a discrete environmental unit consisting of living and nonliving parts that interact to form a stable system. The term can be applied at any scale, from a drop of pond water to the entire biosphere (i.e., the earth can be viewed as a single ecosystem).

Ecosystem services   are goods (such as food) and services (such as waste assimilation) that benefit human populations either directly or indirectly. Ecosystem services are derived from ecosystem functions, which are the biological or system properties and processes of ecosystems.

Eminent domain   is the power of the federal or state government to take private property for a public purpose, even if the property owner objects. The Fifth Amendment to the United States Constitution allows the government to take private property if the taking is for a public use and the owner is "justly compensated" (usually, paid fair market value) for his or her loss. A public use is virtually anything sanctioned by a federal or state legislative body, but such uses may include roads, parks, reservoirs, schools, hospitals, or other public buildings. Sometimes eminent domain is called condemnation, taking, or expropriation.

Erosion   is the loss of sediment from the beach, dunes, and bluffs.

Flooding   is a general and temporary condition of partial or complete inundation of normally dry land areas from the overflow of inland or tidal water, or rapid accumulation or runoff of surface waters from any source.

Geomorphology   is that branch of both physiography and geology that deals with the form of the earth, the general configuration of its surface, and the changes that take place in the evolution of landforms.

Groin   is a shore protection structure built (usually perpendicular to the shoreline) to trap littoral drift or retard erosion of the shore.

Harbor   is any protected water area affording a place of safety for vessels.

Hazard mitigation   is actions taken to reduce or eliminate long-term risk to people and property from hazards and their effects.

Hazard reduction   involves strengthening structures and providing safeguards to reduce the amount of damage caused by natural hazards. Activities include altering the coastal environment through erosion control devices, beach nourishment, flood control works, floodproofing, windproofing, or elevating.

Hurricane   is a tropical cyclone in the Northern Hemisphere with sustained winds of at least 74 miles per hour (64 knots) or greater in the North Atlantic Ocean, Caribbean Sea, or Gulf of Mexico. These winds blow in a large spiral around a relatively calm center of extremely low pressure known as the eye. Around the rim of the eye, winds may gust to more than 200 mph. The entire storm, which can be up to 340 miles (550 kilometers) in diameter, dominates the ocean surface and lower atmosphere over tens of thousands of square miles. Hurricanes draw their energy from the warm surface water of the tropics (usually above 27°C) and latent heat of condensation, which explains why hurricanes dissipate rapidly once they move over cold water or large land masses.

Hurricane straps   are clips at the intersection of a roof and the top of the wall used to keep the roof in place under high wind conditions.

Jetty   is a massive, constructed rock structure built to stabilize and protect harbor entrances, usually built perpendicular to the shore to stabilize a river mouth.

Marginalization   is a social science term that refers to people or groups whose social or economic conditions cause them to be on the outer edges and blocked from full participation in a culture or society.

Mean High Tide   A tidal datum. The average of all the high water heights observed over the National Tidal Datum Epoch. For stations with shorter series, simultaneous observational comparisons are made with a control tide station in order to derive the equivalent datum of the National Tidal Datum Epoch.

Natural hazards   are episodic and chronic destructive natural system events, such as hurricanes, beach erosion, tsunamis, and severe storms.

Northeaster (nor'easter)   is a type of severe winter storm that affects the Mid-Atlantic and New England states.

Overwash   occurs when a portion of the water that rushes up onto the beach following the breaking of a wave carries over the crest of a berm or structure.

Retrofit   is the strengthening of structures to mitigate natural disaster risks.

Revetment   is a sloping surface of stone, concrete, or other material used to protect an embankment, natural coast, or shore structure against erosion by wave action or currents.

Scour   refers to the removal of underwater material by waves and currents, especially at the base or toe of a shore structure.

Shore   is the narrow strip of land in immediate contact with the sea, including the zone between high and low water lines. A shore of unconsolidated material usually is called a beach.

Shoreline   is the intersection of a specified plane of water with the shore or beach. The line delineating the shoreline on National Ocean Service nautical charts and surveys approximates the mean high water line.

Storm (hurricane) shutters   are coverings for windows to protect them from flying debris during a storm event.

Storm surge   is the local change in the elevation of the ocean along a shore due to a storm. The storm surge is measured by subtracting the astronomic tidal elevation from the total elevation. It typically has a duration of a few hours. Because wind-generated waves ride on top of the storm surge (and are not included in the definition), the total instantaneous elevation may exceed greatly the predicted storm surge plus astronomic tide. It is potentially catastrophic, especially on low-lying coasts with gently sloping offshore topography.

Topography   is the configuration of a surface, including its relief and the positions of its streams, roads, buildings, and so on.

Tsunami   is a series of waves generated by an impulsive disturbance in the ocean, usually an earthquake occurring near or under the sea.

Turbidity   occurs when water is thick or opaque with roiled sediment.

Watershed   is the entire region that drains into a river, river system, or water body.

Wetland   is an ecosystem that depends on constant or recurrent shallow inundation or saturation at or near the surface of the substrate.

APPENDIX B

ABOUT THE CONTRIBUTORS
AND THE PROJECT STAFF

THE CONTRIBUTORS

BETTY HEARN MORROW, *Chair*, is the director of the Lab for Social and Behavioral Research and a professor with the Department of Sociology and Anthropology at the International Hurricane Center, Florida International University. Her areas of teaching and research include family sociology, domestic violence, qualitative methodology, and sociology of disaster and gender. Dr. Morrow's recent research has focused on the socioeconomic aspects of natural hazards and disasters, particularly the role and importance of women in disaster planning and impact assessment. She also has published several sociological case studies of Hurricane Andrew and disaster impacts in the Caribbean. Dr. Morrow received a bachelor's degree from Ohio State University, a master's degree from Florida State University, and a doctorate from the University of Miami.

TIMOTHY BEATLEY is an associate professor at the University of Virginia's Department of Urban and Environmental Planning. Dr. Beatley's primary teaching and research interests are in environmental planning and policy, with special emphasis on coastal and natural hazards planning, environmental values and ethics, and biodiversity conservation. He has published extensively in these areas, including several recent books that he has authored or co-authored. In recent years, much of his research and writing has been focused on the subject of sustainable communities in both the United States and Europe. Dr. Beatley received a Ph.D. in city and regional planning from the University of North Carolina at Chapel Hill.

LLOYD S. CLUFF manages the Pacific Gas and Electric Company's Geosciences Department and runs the Earthquake Risk Management Program. He is an expert on the identification of active seismic faults and their potential motions. In this capacity, he assesses PG&E facilities with respect to earthquake and geologic hazards. He also has conducted many post-earthquake field studies and studies the relationship of tectonics, seismic geology, and seismicity of many active fault zones throughout the world. He has authored or co-authored more than 180 technical papers on subjects related to seismic geology, earthquake hazards and risks, and seismic safety of critical facilities. He is a member of the National Academy of Engineering and won the John Wesley Powell Award from the U.S. Geological Survey in 2000. He received a bachelor's degree in geology from the University of Utah.

ROBERT COLLINS is the All-Hazards Planning unit manager for the Florida Department of Community Affair's Division of Emergency Management. He also serves as the state of Florida's hurricane program manager and information and planning emergency support function chief. In this capacity, he manages the efforts of four planners to develop operation plans, collects hazards and vulnerability data, and develops storm tide atlases and hurricane evacuation studies. He has been closely involved with Governor Jeb Bush's Hurricane Evacuation Task Force and is a member of the Evacuation Planning Committee for the National Hurricane Conference. Previously, he worked as a planner for Florida's Division of Resource Planning and Management and an intelligence officer for the United States Army. He received a degree in geography from Virginia Polytechnic Institute and State University.

SUSAN L. CUTTER is a Carolina Distinguished Professor in the Department of Geography at the University of South Carolina and past president of the Association of American Geographers. She also is the founding director of the department's Hazards Research Lab, a research and training center that integrates geographical information processing techniques with hazards management. Dr. Cutter has been working in the hazards field for more than 25 years and is a nationally recognized scholar in this area. She is a Fellow of the American Association for the Advancement of Science and serves on the Advisory Committee for the Division of Earth and Life Sciences of the National Academy of Sciences. She has authored eight books and more than 50 peer-reviewed articles on hazards and environmental themes. She received a Ph.D. in geography from University of Chicago.

LAURIE JOHNSON currently directs Risk Management Solutions' Global Risk Modeling unit, where she leads the company's efforts to develop new Web-based information products on global catastrophes and risks and coordinates catastrophe response efforts, including field reconnaissance, client communications, and event documentation. She has more than 12 years of professional experience in urban planning consulting and research, emphasizing disaster recovery, risk reduction planning, and hazards communication. She is also currently a co-principal investigator on a National Science Foundation study of the factors facilitating and impeding reconstruction in Los Angeles and Kobe, Japan, following the 1994 and 1995 earthquakes, respectively. Prior to joining RMS in 1998, Ms. Johnson was principal urban planner with EQE International and a senior planner with Spangle Associates. She received a B.S. degree in geophysics and a master's degree in urban planning from Texas A&M University.

HOWARD KUNRUETHER is professor and co-director of the Risk Management and Decision Processes Center at The Wharton School at the University of Pennsylvania. Dr. Kunruether's research focuses on the effect of insurance regulatory and liability questions on risk-management decisions, particularly those concerning energy and environmental issues and industrial risk management policies. He brings to the panel special expertise in risk assessment, risk-spreading techniques such as insurance, and strategies for managing risk through loss reduction methods. Dr. Kunruether has served on a number of national boards and committees advising industry and government, and is currently a member of the National Academy of Science's Board on Natural Disasters. Dr. Kunruether received a B.A. from Bates College and a Ph.D. in economics from the Massachusetts Institute of Technology.

ROBERT G. LEE has more than 35 years of experience in law enforcement, private security, and emergency management and holds numerous professional certifications. After retiring from the Los Angeles County Sheriff's Department, he was director of security and safety for May Department Stores and corporate security and emergency management for Great Western Financial Corporation. In 1996, he co-founded Borden/Lee Consulting, which specializes in emergency response planning and management. Mr. Lee has managed responses to, and recovery from, a wide variety of incidents, including riots, earthquakes, firestorms, and hurricanes. He has authored emergency plans for a variety of private and public institutions, and is the author of a best-selling book. He has been a member of many national and international committees and organizations, including the United Nations Committee for Natural Hazard Reduction and two presidential advisory committees. He has served on the Board of Directors of the Business and Industry Council for Emergency Planning and Preparedness since 1984, including four terms as president.

JOSEPHINE MALILAY has been an epidemiologist in natural and technological disaster settings with the U.S. Centers for Disease Control and Prevention (CDC) since 1991. In July 2000, she was designated team leader for the Disaster Epidemiology and Assessment Team, Division of Environmental Hazards and Health Effects, National Center for Environmental Health, CDC. In this capacity,

she designs and conducts epidemiological investigations of public health problems associated with risk to humans from exposures related to acute and natural
hazards; recommends environmental health studies, surveillance programs, emergency response actions and protocols, and prevention and control measures; and
represents the health sector on interagency government committees with activities in natural hazards reduction. She has published numerous articles on the
public health effects of disasters and has conducted numerous national and international post-disaster field investigations. She received a Ph.D. in epidemiology
from Tulane University.

DONNA MOFFITT directs the Division of Coastal Management in the North
Carolina Department of Environment and Natural Resources. She manages a
staff of 61 and a budget of approximately $5 million covering several program
areas, including land use planning, permits and enforcement, federal and state
consistency decisions, public beach access, and the North Carolina Coastal
Reserves. She also serves as executive secretary for the Coastal Resources Commission. Previously, she was the assistant director for nonpoint source programs
in the Division of Soil and Water Conservation, where she administered the
North Carolina Agriculture Cost Share Program and developed a successful $270
million Conservation Reserve Enhancement Program grant. Between 1988 and
1992, she directed the Outer Continental Shelf Office in the Department of
Administration. She received undergraduate and graduate degrees from North
Carolina State University and a law degree from the University of North Carolina
at Chapel Hill.

MICHAEL K. ORBACH is a professor in marine affairs and policy and director
of the Duke University Marine Lab. Dr. Orbach's research interests are in the
application of social and policy sciences to coastal and ocean policy and management. His work uses a cultural, or human, ecology perspective to analyze human
behavior in coastal and ocean environments. His current research projects include
the development and application of limited entry and effort management systems
to marine fisheries, the formation and socioeconomic impact of marine minerals
policy, marine mammal and endangered species–fisheries conflicts, and citizen
involvement in coastal and ocean policy. Dr. Orbach received a Ph.D. in cultural
anthropology from the University of California, San Diego.

DOUGLAS RADER leads Environmental Defense's efforts to protect and restore
North Carolina coastal ecosystems. Dr. Rader is a biologist and conducts technical evaluations of coastal pollution resulting from industrial activities, sewage
treatment plants, and nonpoint sources, specializing in wetlands preservation and
land use policies. He researched potential environmental hazards of raising hogs
in North Carolina both before and after Hurricane Floyd. He is a member of the

North Carolina Governor's Working Group on Mobil Offshore Drilling, and has authored numerous articles and technical reports on estuarine and freshwater ecosystems. He previously worked for the state Division of Environmental Management, where he directed the Albemarle-Pamlico Estuarine Study (1986–1988), led the special projects group (1985–1986), and headed the Resource Evaluation Branch (1985). Dr. Rader received an M.S. in zoology from the University of Washington and a Ph.D. in biology from the University of North Carolina.

JACQUELINE SAVITZ served as executive director of the Coast Alliance, a non-profit organization specializing in coastal pollution and development issues. In this capacity, she authored various reports and articles related to coastal pollution and development. Ms. Savitz recently joined Oceana, a new non-profit organization dedicated to protecting and restoring ocean life. There she directs the Ocean Pollution Campaign. Prior to joining the Coast Alliance, she worked as an environmental policy analyst with the Environmental Working Group in Washington, D.C., and served as an environmental advocate with the Chesapeake Bay Foundation. She has studied, and authored or co-authored numerous reports on, the public health effects of industrial water pollution; air pollution; fish contamination; medical waste disposal; and Chesapeake Bay pollution issues, such as contaminated sediments, brownfields, and point source releases. Ms. Savitz received a bachelor's degree in marine science and biology from the University of Miami and a master's degree in environmental science with emphasis in toxicology from the University of Maryland.

PAUL SCHOLZ joined the National Oceanic and Atmospheric Administration (NOAA) Coastal Services Center in 1994. As a division director for the Coastal Management Services, he manages program development and is responsible for establishing a new, cross-NOAA facility in Hawaii. Mr. Scholz has more than 18 years of experience in project and program development, implementation, management, and evaluation; training design; and facilitation relating to coastal resources, fisheries, aquaculture, and environmental conservation. He was formerly the director of International Coastal Programs for the University of South Carolina, and served as a fisheries extension agent in Ecuador while in the Peace Corps. He received a bachelor's degree in wildlife management from Southern Illinois University at Carbondale and a master's degree in marine science from the University of South Carolina.

MARILYN M. SELF has more than 28 years of experience with the American Red Cross and is currently the disaster health services specialist in the Georgia Field Office. Ms. Self assists all chapters in the state in increasing their preparedness to provide health services staffing in shelters, plan for evacuation of those with special health care needs, provide health services case management, and support families and victims in time of crisis and grief. She has focused on planning for and delivering disaster health services to Red Cross clients and relief workers on hundreds of local events and more than 15 large national disasters. She also coordinated the provision of Red Cross health and mental health services in the aftermath of several violent and mass casualty incidents. She is a member of the Red Cross National Nursing Committee and is the 1995 winner of the Jane Delano award, the highest nursing honor the American Red Cross can give an employee. She is a graduate of the Medical College of Georgia School of Nursing.

DENNIS J. SMITH is the chief of policy and planning for Vermont Emergency Management. In this capacity, he manages a wide range of state level planning initiatives and supervises staff responsible for radiological preparedness planning and hazard mitigation. Previously, Mr. Smith worked for eight years for the Florida Department of Community Affairs. During his tenure in Florida, Mr. Smith developed Operation: Open for Business!, a private-sector mitigation initiative; managed the state hazard mitigation planning programs; served on the team that developed the local mitigation strategy; and provided technical assistance on hazard mitigation. He was the principal author of the *National Emergency Management Association and Council of State Governments' Standard Mitigation Protocols for Interstate Mutual Aid* (1998). Mr. Smith served as an agriculture and environmental science teacher trainer while a Peace Corps volunteer in Liberia. He received a bachelor's degree in environmental studies from Rutgers University, Cook College, and a master's degree in planning from the Florida State University.

HEINZ CENTER STAFF

SHEILA D. DAVID is a Senior Fellow and project manager at The Heinz Center, where she is currently managing studies for the Center's Sustainable Oceans, Coasts, and Waterways Program. She has been the study manager for two other Heinz Center projects: *Dam Removal: Science and Decision Making* (2002) and *The Hidden Costs of Coastal Hazards* (2001). Prior to joining The Heinz Center in 1997, she was a senior program officer at the National Research Council's (NRC) Water Science and Technology Board for 21 years, where she was the study director for approximately 30 committees that produced reports on topics such as managing coastal erosion, restoration of aquatic ecosystems, protection of groundwater, wetlands characteristics and boundaries, water quality and reuse, natural resource protection in the Grand Canyon, and sustainable water supplies in the Middle East. Ms. David has served as an advisor and board member of the Association for Women in Science (AWIS) and as editor of AWIS magazine. She is also a founder of the NAS annual program honoring women in science.

SARAH K. BAISH was a research associate for The Heinz Center's Sustainable Oceans, Coasts, and Waterways program. Currently, Ms. Baish is pursuing a master's degree in urban and environmental planning at the University of Virginia. Prior to joining the Center, she worked in a national park in Slovakia as an environmental management consultant with the Peace Corps. Her primary responsibilities included grant writing, organizing educational events, promoting interpretive visitor services, and establishing international collaborations. Previously, she interned with the National Oceanic and Atmospheric Administration, and her work contributed to the establishment of a humpback whale sanctuary in Hawaii. She received a B.A. in environmental science from the University of Virginia.

JUDY GOSS is a research assistant for The Heinz Center's Sustainable Oceans, Coasts, and Waterways program. She graduated *cum laude* with a degree in political science from Mary Washington College in 2001. She also works for Mary Washington as a part-time assistant debate coach. She is particularly interested in the intersection of gender and political communication and plans to pursue a graduate degree in communication studies.

REFERENCES

Acker, J. 1991. Hierarchies, jobs, bodies: A theory of gendered organizations, pp. 162–179. In The social consequences of gender, J. Lorber and S. Farrell, eds. Newbury, CA: Sage.

Adola, F. O. 1999. Natural disaster episode: Impacts, emergency response, and health effects of Hurricane Georges in the Gulf Coast. Quick Response Report #122. http://www.colorado.edu/hazards/qr/qr122/qr122.html. Jan. 2, 2001.

Albemarle-Pamlico Estuarine Study. 1994. Comprehensive conservation and management plan. http://www2.ncsu.edu/ncsu/CIL/WRRI/neuseapes.html.

Alexander, D. 1993. Natural disasters. New York: Chapman & Hall.

American Psychiatric Association. 2000. Public information series: When disaster strikes. http://www.psych.org/public_info/disaster.cfm.

Anderson, M.B. 2000. Vulnerability to disaster and sustainable development: A general framework for assessing vulnerability, pp. 11–25. In Storms, Volume I, R. Pielke, Jr. and R. Pielke, Sr., eds. London: Routledge Press.

Baia, C. 2001. Personal communication from C. Baia, economic development coordinator, city of Deerfield Beach, to Dennis Smith. Oct. 2, 2001.

Bales, J., C.J. Oblinger, and A. H. Sallenger. 2000. Two months of flooding in North Carolina, September–October 1999: Hydrologic water-quality, and geologic effects of hurricanes Dennis, Floyd, and Irene. Water Resources Investigations Report 00-4093. Raleigh, NC: U.S. Geological Survey. http://water.usgs.gov/pubs/wri/wri004093/.

Balluz, L., D. Moll, M.G. Diaz Martinez, J.E. Merida Colindres, and J. Malilay. 2001. Environmental pesticide exposure in Honduras following Hurricane Mitch. Bulletin of the World Health Organization 79(4): 288–295.

Barnes, J. 1998. Florida's hurricane history. Chapel Hill: University of North Carolina Press.

Bates, F.L., C. Fogleman, V. Parenton, R. Pittman, and G. Tracy. 1963. The social and psychological consequences of a natural disaster: A longitudinal study of Hurricane Audrey. Washington, DC: National Research Council.

Beatley, T., D. Brower, and A. Schwab. 1994. An introduction to coastal zone management. Washington, DC: Island Press.

Birkland, T.A. 1997. After disaster, agenda setting, public policy, and focusing events. Washington, DC: Georgetown University Press.

Blaikie, P., T. Cannon, I. David, and B. Wisner. 1994. At risk: Natural hazards, people's vulnerability, and disasters. London: Routledge Press.

Bolin, R. 1993. Household and community recovery after earthquakes. Boulder, CO: University of Colorado, Institute of Behavioral Science.

Bolin, R.C. 1985. Disasters and long-term recovery policy: A focus on housing and families. Policy Studies Review 4(4): 704–715.

Bolin, R.C., and P. Bolton. 1986. Race, religion, and ethnicity in disaster recovery. Boulder, CO: University of Colorado.

Bolin, R., and L. Stanford. 1991. Shelter, housing and recovery: A comparison of U.S. disasters. Disasters 15(1): 24–34.

Bolin, R., with L. Stanford. 1998. The Northridge earthquake: Vulnerability and disaster. London: Routledge Press.

Boore, J.A., and L. Aptekar. 1990. The emotional effects of disaster on children: A review of the literature. International Journal of Mental Health 19: 77–90.

Boyce, J.K. 2000. Let them eat risk? Wealth, rights and disaster vulnerability. Disasters 24(3): 254–261.

Brauer M. 1999. Health impacts of biomass air pollution. In Health guidelines for vegetation fire events, D.H. Schwela, J.G. Goldammer, L.H. Morawska, and O. Simpson, eds. Singapore: Institute of Environmental Epidemiology, Ministry of Health. http://www.who.int./peh/air/vegetation_fires.htm.

Brewer, R.D., P.D. Morris, and T.B. Cole. 1994. Hurricane-related emergency department visits in an inland area: An analysis of the public health impact of Hurricane Hugo in North Carolina. Annals of Emergency Medicine 23(4): 731–736.

Brown D.L. 1999. Disparate effects of the 1989 Loma Prieta and 1994 Northridge earthquakes on hospital admissions for acute myocardial infarction: Importance of superimposition of triggers. American Heart Journal 7(5): 830–836.

Brunckhorst D.J., and P. Bridgewater. 1996. A novel approach to identifying and select care reserve networks and to apply UNESCO biosphere principles to the coastal marine world. In Marine protected areas and biosphere reserves: Towards a new paradigm. Canberra, Australia: ANCA/UNESCO: 12–17.

Burby, R. 1992. Sharing environmental risks. Boulder, CO: Westview Press.

Burke, J.D., P. Moccia, J.F. Borus, and B.J. Burns. 1986. Emotional distress in fifth-grade children 10 months after a natural disaster. Journal of the American Academy of Child Psychiatry 25(4): 536–541.

Burton, I., R.W. Kates, and G.F. White. 1993. The environment as hazard. New York: Guildford.

Burwell, N.Y. 2001. Looking into the face of the storm: African Americans, pp. 149–150. In Facing our future: Hurricane Floyd and recovery in the coastal plain, J.R. Maiolo, J.C. Whitehead, M. McGee, L. King, J. Johnson, and H. Stone, eds.. Wilmington, NC: Coastal Carolina Press.

California Seismic Safety Commission. 1991. Loma Prieta's call to action. Sacramento, CA.

Center for Mental Health Services. 2000. Psychosocial issues for children and adolescents in disaster. Washington, DC.

Centers for Disease Control and Prevention. 2000. Morbidity and mortality associated with Hurricane Floyd–North Carolina, September–October 1999. Morbidity and Mortality Weekly Report 49(17): 369–372.

Centers for Disease Control and Prevention. 1993. Injuries and illnesses related to Hurricane Andrew—Louisiana, 1992. Morbidity and Mortality Weekly Report 42:242–243, 249–251.

Comfort, L., B. Wisner, S. Cutter, R. Pulwarty, K. Hewitt, A. Oliver-Smith, J. Weiner, M. Fordham, W. Peacock, and F. Krimgold, 1999. Reframing disaster policy: The global evolution of vulnerable communities. Environmental Hazards 1(1): 39–44.

Costanza, R., R. d'Arge, R. de Groots, S. Farber, M. Grasso, B. Hannon, K. Limburg, S. Naeem, R.V. O'Neill, J. Paruelo, R.G. Raskin, P. Sutton, and M. van den Belt. 1997. The value of the world's ecosystem services and natural capital. Nature 38(7): 253–260.

Council of State and Territorial Epidemiologists (United States). 1998. Position statement EH-1: Proposal to adopt new or amended surveillance definitions for four environmental conditions. Data presented at the 1998 CSTE Annual Meeting. http://www.cste.org/ps/1998/1998-eh-01.htm. Accessed September 17, 2002.

Cova, T.J., and R.L. Church. 1997. Modeling community evacuation vulnerability using GIS. International Journal of Geographical Information Science 11(8): 763–784.

Cutter, S.L., ed. 2001. American hazardscapes: The regionalization of hazards and disasters. Washington, DC: Joseph Henry Press.

Cutter, S.L. 1996. Vulnerability to environmental hazards. Progress in Human Geography 20(4): 529–539.

Cutter, S.L., B. Boruff, and W.L. Shirley. 2001. Indicators of social vulnerability to hazards. Unpublished paper. Columbia, SC: University of South Carolina, Hazards Research Lab.

Cutter, S.L., J.T. Mitchell, and M.S. Scott. 2000. Revealing the vulnerability of people and places: A case study of Georgetown county, South Carolina. Annals of the Association of American Geographers 90(4): 713–737.

Dash N., W.G. Peacock, and B.H. Morrow. 2000. And the poor get poorer: A neglected black community, pp. 206–225. In Hurricane Andrew: Ethnicity, gender, and sociology of disaster, W.G. Peacock, B.H. Morrow, and H. Gladwin, eds. Miami: Florida International University, International Hurricane Center.

Davis, K.M., and M.G. Ender. 1999. The 1997 Red River Valley Flood: Impact on marital relationships. Applied Behavioral Science Review 7(2): 181–188.

Dean, C. 1999. Against the tide: The battle for America's beaches. New York: Columbia University Press.

Delia, A.A. 2001. Population and economic changes in eastern North Carolina before and after Hurricane Floyd, pp. 199–204. In Facing our future: Hurricane Floyd and recovery in the coastal plain, J.R. Maiolo, J.C. Whitehead, M. McGee, L. King, J. Johnson, and H. Stone, eds. Wilmington, NC: Coastal Carolina Press.

Downton, M, and R. Pielke, Jr. 2001. Discretion without accountability: Politics, flood damage, and climate. Natural Hazards Review 2(4) 157–166.

Drabek, T.E. 1996. Disaster evacuation behavior: Tourists and other transients. Boulder, CO: University of Colorado, Institute of Behavioral Science.

Duke University Program for the Study of Developed Shorelines. 2002. Beach Nourishment Database. http://www.env.duke.edu/psds/nourishment.htm. Accessed September 17, 2002.

Ebert, C.H.V. 2000. Disasters: An analysis of natural and human-induced hazards, 4th Ed. Dubuque, IA: Kendall Hunt.

Eguchi, R.T., J.D. Goltz, C.E. Taylor, S.E. Chang, P.J. Flores, L.A. Johnson, H.A. Seligson, and N.C. Blais. 1996. The Northridge earthquake: Analyzing economic impacts and recovery from urban earthquakes, Issues for policymakers. Oakland, CA: Earthquake Engineering Research Institute.

Elsner, J.B., and A.B. Kara. 1999. Hurricanes of the North Atlantic: Climate and society. Oxford, UK: Oxford University Press.

Enarson, E. 2000. "We will make meaning out of this": Women's cultural response to the Red River Valley flood. International Journal of Mass Emergencies and Disasters 18(1):39–62.

Enarson, E. 1999. Women and housing issues in U.S. disasters: Case studies from Hurricane Andrew and the Red River Valley flood. International Journal of Mass Emergencies and Disasters 17(1): 39–64.

Enarson, E., and B.H. Morrow. 1998. The gendered terrain of disasters: Through women's eyes. Miami: Florida International University, International Hurricane Center.

Enarson, E., and B. H. Morrow. 2000. A gendered perspective: Through the eyes of women, pp. 16–140. In Hurricane Andrew: Ethnicity, gender, and the sociology of disaster, W.G. Peacock, B.H. Morrow, and H. Gladwin, eds. Miami: Florida International University, International Hurricane Center.

Enarson, E., and J. Scanlon. 1999. Gender patterns in flood evacuation: A case study in Canada's Red River Valley. Applied Behavioral Science Review 7(2): 103–124.

Erikson, K. 1994. A new species of trouble: Explorations in disaster, trauma, and community. New York: W.W. Norton.

Escobar, J.I., G. Canino, M. Rubio-Stipec, and M. Bravo. 1992. Somatic symptoms after a natural disaster: A prospective study. American Journal of Psychiatry 149:965–967.

Esnard, A.M. 2001. Taking stock of quality of life during post-disaster recovery. Natural Hazards Observer XXV(6): 10–11.

Farberow, N.L., and N.S. Gordon. 1981. Manual for child health workers in major disasters. Rockville, MD: Department of Health and Human Services ADM 81-1070.

Federal Emergency Management Agency. 2001a. Total Major Disaster Declarations. http://www.fema.gov/library/diz01.shtm. Accessed September 17, 2002.

Federal Emergency Management Agency. 2001b. Hazus 99: Estimated annualized earthquake losses for the United States. http://www.fema.gov/hazus/eq_est.htm. Accessed September 17, 2002.

Federal Emergency Management Agency. 2001c. Hurricane Floyd disaster response update. http://www.app1.fema.gov/hu99/99246.htm. Accessed September 17, 2002.

Federal Emergency Management Agency. 1997. Disasters: A deadly and costly toll around the world. http://www.fema.gov/pdf/library/stats.pdf. Accessed September 17, 2002.

Federal Emergency Management Agency. 1995. National mitigation strategy: Partnerships for building safer communities. Washington, DC.

Fitts, W. 2001. "Looking into the Face of the Storm: Small Businesses." Pp. 205–206 in J.R. Maiolo, J.C. Whitehead, M. McGee, L. King, J. Johnson and H. Stone (Eds.) Facing Our Future: Hurricane Floyd and Recovery in the Coastal Plain. Wilmington, NC: Coastal Carolina Press.

Fothergill, A. 1999. An exploratory study of woman battering in the Grand Forks flood disaster: Implications for community responses and policies. International Journal of Mass Emergencies and Disasters 17(1): 79–98.

Fothergill, A. 1996. Gender, risk, and disaster. International Journal of Mass Emergencies and Disasters 14(1): 33–56.

French, S., and G. Rudholm. 1990. Damage to public property in the Whittier Narrows earthquake: Implications for earthquake insurance. Earthquake Spectra 6(1):105–123.

Gallagher, T. 1993. The Florida Department of Insurance: Hurricane Andrew's impact on insurance in the state of Florida. Ft. Lauderdale, FL: Florida Department of Insurance.

Geis, D.E. 2000. By design: The disaster resilient and quality of life community. Natural Hazards Review 1(3): 151–160.

Gladwin, H., and W.G. Peacock. 2000. Warning and evacuation: A night for hard houses, pp. 191–205. In Hurricane Andrew: Ethnicity, gender, and the sociology of disasters, W.G. Peacock, B.H. Morrow, and H. Gladwin, eds. Miami: Florida International University, International Hurricane Center.

Godschalk, D., and D. Salveson. Undated. Development on coastal barriers: Does the Coastal Barriers Resources Act make a difference? Report to the Coastal Alliance, Washington, DC.

Green, B.L., M. Korol, M.C. Grace, M.G. Vary, A. Leonard, G.C. Gleser, and S. Smitson-Cohen. 1991. Children and disaster: Age, gender, and parental effects on PTSD symptoms. Journal of the American Academy of Child and Adolescent Psychiatry 30(6): 945–951.

Hazards Workshop Summary #16. 2000. Disasters, diversity, and equity. S00-16. http://www.colorado.edu/hazards/ss/ss00/s16.html. Boulder, CO: Natural Hazards Center, University of Colorado.

Healy, B. 2001. Health bytes: Mental health effects of disasters. https://corpweb.redcross.org/exec/presoffice/hlthbytes/070301.html.

Hebert, P.J., J.D. Jarrell, and M. Maxfield. 1996. The deadliest, costliest, and most intense United States hurricanes of this century (and other frequently requested hurricane facts), NOAA Technical Memorandum NWS TPC-1 (February). Miami: National Hurricane Center.

Hedrick, C. 2000. State, territory, and commonwealth beach nourishment programs: A national overview. Office of Ocean and Coastal Research Management Program Policy Series, Technical Document No. 00-01. Available online at http://www.ocrm.nos.noaa.gov/pdf/finalbeach.pdf

Heinz Center. 2000a. Evaluation of erosion hazards. Washington, DC. Also available at http://www.heinzcenter.org.

Heinz Center. 2000b. The hidden costs of coastal hazards: Implications for risk assessment and mitigation. Covelo, CA: Island Press.

Hewitt, K. 2000. Safe place or "catastrophic society"? Perspectives on hazards and disasters in Canada. The Canadian Geographer 44(4): 325–341.

Hewitt, K. 1997. Regions of risk: A geographical introduction to disasters. Essex, UK: Longman.

Hochschild, A.1989. Second shift: Working parents and the revolution at home. New York: Viking Press.

Howard, Joann. 1999. 24th Annual Workshop on Hazards Research and Applications. Speech. http://www.fema.gov/nfip/jahsp5.htm. July 13, 1999.

Huerta, F., and R. Horton. 1978. Coping behavior of elderly flood victims. The Gerontologist 18:541–546.

Insurance Institute for Property Loss Reduction and Insurance Research Council (IIPLR and IRC). 1995. Community exposure and community protection: Hurricane Andrew's legacy. Wheaton, IL and Boston: IIPLR and IRC.

Institute for Business and Home Safety. 2001. Lessons from PPP2000: Living with earth's extremes. Report from the PPP2000 Working Group to the Office of Science and Technology Policy, Subcommittee on Natural Disaster Reduction. Tampa, FL.

Institute for Business and Home Safety. 1998. The insured cost of natural disasters: A report on the IBHS paid loss database. Boston, MA.

Insurance Services Office, Inc. 2000. Hurricane Floyd toll rises to 1.8 billion, up 500 million from initial estimates, in ISO's resurveys of insurer's losses. Press Release, December 6, 2000. http://www.iso.com/press_releases/1999/12_06_99.html. Accessed September 17, 2002.

Interagency Floodplain Management Review Committee. 1994. Sharing the challenge: Floodplain management into the 21st century. Report to the administration of the Federal Interagency Floodplain Management Task Force. Washington, DC.

Jacobson, J., J. Lee, and J. Malilay. 2000. Disaster-related deaths in the United States, 1994–1998. Unpublished data presented at the Centers for Disease Control and Prevention, Epidemiology Rounds, Atlanta, Georgia, January 2000.

Jagger, T., J.B. Elsner, and Y. Niu. 2001. A dynamic probability model of hurricane winds in coastal counties of the United States. Journal of Applied Meteorology 40:853–863.

Janerich, D.T., A.D. Stark, P. Greenwald, W.S. Burnett, H.I. Jacobson, and J. McCusker. 1981. Increased leukemia, lymphoma, and spontaneous abortion in western New York following a flood disaster. Public Health Reports 96: 350–356.

Johnson, J., and M. Orbach, 1991. The impact of urbanization on Florida's spiny lobster fishery. City and Society 2(1): 95–112.

Jones, R.T., R. Frary, P. Cunningham, and J.D. Weddle. 1993. The psychological effects of Hurricane Andrew on elementary and middle school children. Boulder, CO: University of Colorado, Natural Hazards Research and Applications Information Center.

Kennedy, D. 2002. Science, terrorism, and natural disasters. Science 295(5554): 405.

Klee, G. A. 1999. The coastal environment: Toward integrated coastal and marine sanctuary management. Upper Saddle River, NJ: Prentice-Hall.

Kriner, S. 2000. One year later: Emotional burdens slow Venezuelan recovery. Disaster Relief: Worldwide Disaster Aid and Information via the Internet. http://www.disasterrelief.org/Disasters/001220venezuelaanniv2. Accessed September 17, 2002.

Krug, E.G., M.J. Kresnow, J. Peddicord, L. Dahlberg, K. Powell, A. Crosby, and J. Annest. 1998. Suicide after natural disasters. New England Journal of Medicine 338(6): 373–378.

Kunreuther, H. 2002. The role of insurance in managing extreme events. Implications for terrorism coverage. Business Economics, April.

Kunreuther, H. 2001. Risk analysis and risk management in an uncertain world. Center for Financial Institutions Working Papers. http://opim.wharton.upenn.edu/risk/downloads/02-08-HK.pdf. Accessed September 17, 2002.

Kunreuther, H., and R. Roth, eds. 1998. Paying the price: The status and role of insurance against natural disasters in the United. States. Washington, DC: Joseph Henry Press.

League of Red Cross and Red Crescent Societies. 1991. Working with women in emergency relief and rehabilitation programmes. Field Studies Paper No. 2. Geneva, Switzerland.

Leatherman, S.P. 2001. Social and economic costs of sea level rise, pp. 181–222. In Sea level rise: History and consequences, edited by B.C. Douglas, M.S. Kearney, and S.P. Leatherman. San Diego: Academic Press.

Leatherman, S.P., K. Zhang, and B. C. Douglas. 2000. Sea level rise shown to drive coastal erosion. EOS Trans. AGU 81(6): 55–57.

Lecomte, E., and K. Gahagan. 1998. Hurricane protection insurance in Florida, pp. 97–124. In Paying the price: The status and role of insurance against natural disasters in the United States. Washington DC: Joseph Henry Press.

Lee, L.E., V. Fonseca, K.M. Brett, J. Sanchez, R.C. Mullen, and L.E. Quenemoen. 1993. Active morbidity surveillance after Hurricane Andrew— Florida, 1992. Journal of the American Medical Association 270:591– 594.

Litan, R., F. Krimgold, K. Clark, and J. Khadlikar.1992. Physical damage and human loss: The economic impact of earthquake mitigation measures. Washington, DC: The Earthquake Project.

Lutgendorf, S.K., M.H. Antoni, G. Ironson, M.A. Fletcher, F. Penedo, A. Baum, N. Schneiderman, and N. Klimas. 1995. Physical symptoms of chronic fatigue syndrome are exacerbated by the stress of Hurricane Andrew. Psychosomatic Medicine 57:310–323.

Lystad, M. 1985. Innovations in mental health services to disaster victims. Washington DC: U.S. Government Printing Office.

Mainster, S. 1998. Personal communication from Steve Mainster to B.H. Morrow, Centro Campesino, Miami, Florida.

Maiolo, J.R., and H. Stone. 2001. Lessons learned, alternative paths to recovery, and specific recommendations, pp. 299–310. In Facing our future: Hurricane Floyd and recovery in the coastal plain, J.R. Maiolo, J.C. Whitehead, M. McGee, L. King, J. Johnson, and H. Stone, eds. Wilmington, NC: Coastal Carolina Press.

Maiolo, J.R., J. C. Whitehead, M. McGee, L. King, J. Johnson, and H. Stone, eds. 2001. Facing our future: Hurricane Floyd and recovery in the coastal plain. Greenville, NC: Coastal Carolina Press.

Mallin, M.A., M.H. Posey, G.C. Shank, M.R. McIver, S.H. Ensign, and T.D. Alphin. 1999. Hurricane effects on water quality and benthos in the Cape Fear Watershed: Natural and anthropogenic impacts. Ecological Applications 9: 350–362.

Mallin, M.A., K.E. Williams, E.C. Esham, and R.P. Lowe. 2000. Effect of human development on bacteriological water quality in coastal watersheds. Ecological Applications 10:1047–1056.

Marks, M. 1993. Storm displaced students homesick for Homestead, p. A1, A15. Miami Herald, June 15.

Mellman, T.A., D. David, J. Kulick-Bell, J. Hebding and B. Nolan. 1995. Sleep disturbances and its relationship to psychiatric morbidity after Hurricane Andrew. American Journal of Psychiatry 152(11): 1659–1663.

Mileti, D. 1999. Disasters by design: A reassessment of natural hazards in the United States. Washington DC: Joseph Henry Press.

Miller, M.L., and J. Auyong. 1991. Coastal zone tourism: A potent force affecting environment and society. Marine Policy 5(2): 75–99.

Minami J., Y. Kawano, T. Ishimitsu, H. Yoshimi, and S. Takishita. 1997. Effect of the Hanshin-Awaji earthquake on blood pressure in patients with essential hypertension. Hypertension 10(2): 222–225.

Mittler, E. 1998. A case study of the enactment of a state building code in South Carolina. Natural Hazards Working Research paper #97. http://www.colorado.edu/hazards/wp/wp97.html.

Morrow, B.H. 1999. Identifying and mapping community vulnerability. Disasters 23(1): 1–18.

Morrow, B.H. 2000. Stretching the bonds: The families of Andrew, pp. 141–170. In Hurricane Andrew: Ethnicity, gender, and the sociology of disasters, W.G. Peacock, B.H. Morrow, and H. Gladwin, eds. Miami: Florida International University, International Hurricane Center.

Morrow, B.H., and W. G. Peacock. 2000. Disasters and social change: The reshaping of Miami, pp. 226–242. In Hurricane Andrew: Ethnicity, gender, and the sociology of disasters, W.G. Peacock, B.H. Morrow, and H. Gladwin, eds. Miami: Florida International University, International Hurricane Center.

Morrow, B.H., and E. Enarson. 1996. Hurricane Andrew through women's eyes: Issues and recommendations. International Journal of Mass Emergencies and Disasters 14(1): 5–22.

Morrow, B.H., and B. Phillips. 1999. What's gender 'got to do with it'? International Journal of Mass Emergencies and Disasters 17(1): 5–11.

National Oceanic and Atmospheric Administration. 2001. Turning to the sea: America's ocean future. http://www.publicaffairs.noaa.gov/oceanreport/tourism.html. November 8.

National Oceanic and Atmospheric Administration. 1998. Trends in U.S. coastal regions, 1970–1998. Addendum to the proceedings, Trends and future challenges for U.S. national ocean and coastal policy. Silver Spring, MD: NOAA, National Ocean Service.

National Weather Service. 1993. Hurricane! A familiarization booklet. Silver Spring, MD. NOAA: PA 91001. http://205.156.54.206/om/brochures/hurfam.pdf.

National Wildlife Federation. 2000. Higher ground: A report on voluntary property buyouts in the nation's floodplains. Washington, DC.

Natural Hazards Caucus Work Group. 2001. Discussion paper for the Congressional Natural Hazards Caucus. Available online at http://www.agiweb.org/workgroup/discussion_paper0101.html.

Neal, P. 1997. On 5th anniversary, Andrew survivors take stock. Reuters News Service, Aug. 23. http://www.cnn.com/WEATHER/9708/23/hurricane.andrew/. Accessed September 17, 2002.

Ngo, E.B. 2001. When disasters and age collide: Reviewing vulnerability of the elderly. Natural Hazards Review 2(2): 80–89.

Noji, E.K., ed. 1997. The public health consequences of disasters. New York: Oxford University Press.

O'Brien, P., and D. Mileti. 1992. Citizen participation in emergency response following the Loma Prieta earthquake. International Journal of Mass Emergencies and Disasters 10(1): 71–89.

Olson, R.S. 2000. Toward a politics of disaster: Losses, values, agendas, and blame. International Journal of Mass Emergencies and Disasters 18(2): 265–287.

Olson, R. S., and R.A. Olson. 1993. "The rubble's standing up" in Oroville, California: The politics of building safety. International Journal of Mass Disasters and Emergencies 11:163–188.

Olson, R.S., R.A. Olson, and V.T. Gawronski. 1998. Night and day: Mitigation policymaking in Oakland, California, before and after the Loma Prieta disaster. International Journal of Mass Emergencies and Disasters 16(2): 145–179.

Olson, R.S., R.A. Olson, and V.T. Gawronski. 1999. Some buildings just can't dance: Politics, life safety, and disaster. Stamford, CT: JAI Press.

Organization of American States. 1990. Disasters, planning, and development: Managing natural hazards to reduce loss. Washington, DC: OAS, Department of Regional Development and Environment, Executive Secretariat for Economic and Social Affairs.

Parati, G., R. Antonicelli, F. Guazzarotti, E. Paciaroni, and G. Mancia. 2001. Cardiovascular effects of an earthquake: Direct evidence by ambulatory bloodpressure monitoring. Hypertension 38(5): 1093–1095.

Parker J., L.E. Bahrick, B. Lundy, R. Fivush, and M. Levitt. (1997). Effects of stress on children's memory for a natural disaster. In C.P. Thompson, D.J. Hermann, J.D. Read, D. Bruce, D.G. Payne, and M.P. Toglia (Eds.), Eyewitness Memory: Theoretical and Applied Perspectives (pp. 31–54). Hillsdale, NJ: Erlbaum Associates.

Pasch, R.J., T.B. Kimberlain, and S.R. Stewart. 1999. Preliminary report, Hurricane Floyd 7–17 September 1999. Silver Spring, MD: National Oceanic and Atmospheric Administration, National Hurricane Center. Available online at http://www.nhc.noaa.gov/1999floyd.html. Accessed September 17, 2002.

Peacock, W.G., and C. Girard. 2000. Ethnic and racial inequalities in disaster damage and insurance settlements, pp.171–190. In Hurricane Andrew: Ethnicity, gender, and the sociology of disasters, W.G. Peacock, B.H. Morrow, and H. Gladwin, eds. Miami: Florida International University, International Hurricane Center.

Peacock, W., B.H. Morrow, and H. Gladwin, eds. 2000. Hurricane Andrew and the reshaping of Miami: Ethnicity, gender, and the socio-political ecology of disasters. Miami: Florida International University, International Hurricane Center.

Peacock, W.G., B.H. Morrow, and H. Gladwin. 2001. Hurricane mitigation and Florida's single family homeowners: A statewide investigation. Miami: Florida International University, International Hurricane Center, Lab for Social and Behavioral Research.

Peacock, W.G., and B.H. Morrow. 2000. Disasters and social change: Hurricane Andrew and the reshaping of Miami?, pp. 226–242. In Hurricane Andrew: Ethnicity, gender, and the sociology of disasters, W.G. Peacock, B.H. Morrow, and H. Gladwin, eds. Miami: Florida International University, International Hurricane Center.

Peacock, W.G, A.K. Ragsdale. 2000. Social systems, ecological networks, and disasters: Toward a socio-political ecology of disasters, pp. 20–35. In Hurricane Andrew: Ethnicity, gender, and the sociology of disasters, W.G. Peacock, B.H. Morrow, and H. Gladwin, eds. Miami: Florida International University, International Hurricane Center.

Phillips, B.D. 2002. Understanding vulnerability. Natural Hazards Observer. January. Available online at http://www.colorado.edu/hazards/o/jano02/jano02d.htm.

Phillips, B.D. 1993. Cultural diversity in disasters: Sheltering, housing, and long-term recovery. International Journal of Mass Emergencies and Disasters 11(1): 99–110.

Pielke R.A., Jr., and C.W. Landsea. 1999. La Niña, El Niño, and Atlantic hurricane damages in the United States. Bulletin of the American Meteorological Society 80(10): 2027–2033.

Platt, R. 1999. Disasters and democracy. Washington, DC: Island Press.

Platt, R. 1995. Lifelines: An emergency management priority for the United States in the 1990s. Disasters 15:172–176.

Polny, M.J. 1993. Recovery after action report. FEMA-0955-DR-FL. Atlanta, GA: Federal Emergency Management Agency.

Provenzo, E.F., Jr., and S.H. Fradd. 1995. Hurricane Andrew, the public schools and the rebuilding of community. Albany: State University of New York.

Puente, S. 1999. Social vulnerability to disaster in Mexico City, pp. 295–334. In Crucibles of hazard: Mega-cities and disasters in transition, J.K. Mitchell, ed. Tokyo: United Nations University Press.

Pulido, L. 2000. Rethinking environmental racism: White privilege and urban development in Southern California. Annals of the Association of American Geographers 90(1): 12–40.

Quinn, B., R. Baker, and J. Pratt. 1994. Hurricane Andrew and a pediatric emergency department. Annals of Emergency Medicine 23:737–741.

Rekenthaler, D., Jr. 1999. North Carolina rains finally end, but real work only beginning. http://www.disasterrelief.org/Disasters/990930Floyd15/. Oct. 6, 1999.

Russell, D.W., and C.E. Cutrona. 1991. Social support, stress and depressive symptoms among the elderly: Test of a process model. Journal of Psychology and Aging 6(2): 190–201.

Schwab, A.K. 2000. Preventing disasters through "hazard mitigation." Popular Government 65(3): 3–12.

Shannon, M.P., C.J. Lonigan, A.J. Finch, Jr., and C.M. Taylor. 1994. Children exposed to a disaster: I. Epidemiology of post-traumatic symptom profiles. Journal of the American Academy of Child and Adolescent Psychiatry 33(1): 80–93.

Shaw, R. 1989. Living with floods in Bangladesh. Anthropology Today, 5(1): 11–13.

Showalter, P.S., and M.F. Myers. 1994. Natural disasters in the United States as release agents of oil, chemicals, or radiological materials 1980–1989: Analysis and recommendations. Risk Analysis 14(2): 169–182.

Sibley, D. 1995. Geographies of exclusion: Society and differences in the West. London: Routledge Press.

Slovic, P., J. Monahan, and D.G. MacGregor. 2000. Violence risk assessment and risk communication: The effects of using actual cases, providing instruction, and employing probability versus frequency formats. Law and Human Behavior 24(3): 271–296.

Small Business Administration. 2002. Basic facts about SBA disaster loan programs. Available online at http://www.sba.gov/gopher/Disaster/General-Information-And-Publications/dad1.txt.

Solomon, S. and B. Green. 1992. Mental health effects of natural and human-made disasters. PTSD Research Quarterly 1(3): 1–7.

Sylves, R. 1996. The politics and administration of presidential disaster declarations: The California floods of winter 1995. Boulder. CO: University of Colorado, Institute of Behavioral Science.

Tobin, G.A., and J.C. Ollenburger. 1993. Natural hazards and the elderly. Boulder, CO: University of Colorado, Natural Hazards Research and Applications Information Center.

U.S. Bureau of the Census. 2000. Metropolitan area and central city population estimates for July 1, 1998: Revised April 1, 1990. http://ceq.eh.doe.gov/nepa/reports/statistics/tab1x4.html. Accessed September 17, 2002.

Van Willigen, M. 2001. Do disasters affect individuals' psychological well-being? An over-time analysis of the effect of Hurricane Floyd on men and women in Eastern North Carolina. International Journal of Mass Emergencies and Disasters 19(1): 40–65.

Vernberg, E.M, A. M. La Greca, W.K. Silverman, and M.J. Prinstein. 1996. Prediction of post-traumatic stress syndrome in children after Hurricane Andrew. Journal of Abnormal Psychology 105:237–248.

Weaver, J. 1995. Disasters: Mental health interventions. Sarasota, FL: Professional Resource Press.

Webb, G.R., K.J. Tierney, and J.M. Dahlmaner. 2000. Business and disasters: Empirical patterns and unanswered questions. Natural Hazards Review 1(2): 83.

Wenk, E., Jr. 1972. The politics of the ocean. Seattle, WA: University of Washington Press.

Whitehead, J.C., B. Edwards, M. Van Willigen, J.R. Maiolo, and K. Wilson. 2001. Hurricane evacuation behavior of coastal North Carolina residents during Bonnie, Dennis, and Floyd, pp. 89–98. In Facing our Future: Hurricane Floyd and recovery in the coastal plain. Greeneville: Coastal Carolina Press, East Carolina University.

Wiest, R., J. Mocellin, and D.T. Motsisi. 1994. The needs of women in disasters and emergencies. Technical report for the United Nations Disaster Management Training Programme. Manitoba, Canada: University of Manitoba.

Wilson, J. 1999. Professionalization and gender in emergency management. International Journal of Mass Emergencies and Disasters 17(1): 111–122.

Wilson, J., B. Phillips, and D. Neal. 1998. Domestic violence after disaster, pp. 115–124. In The gendered terrain of disasters: Through women's eyes. Miami: Florida International University, International Hurricane Center.